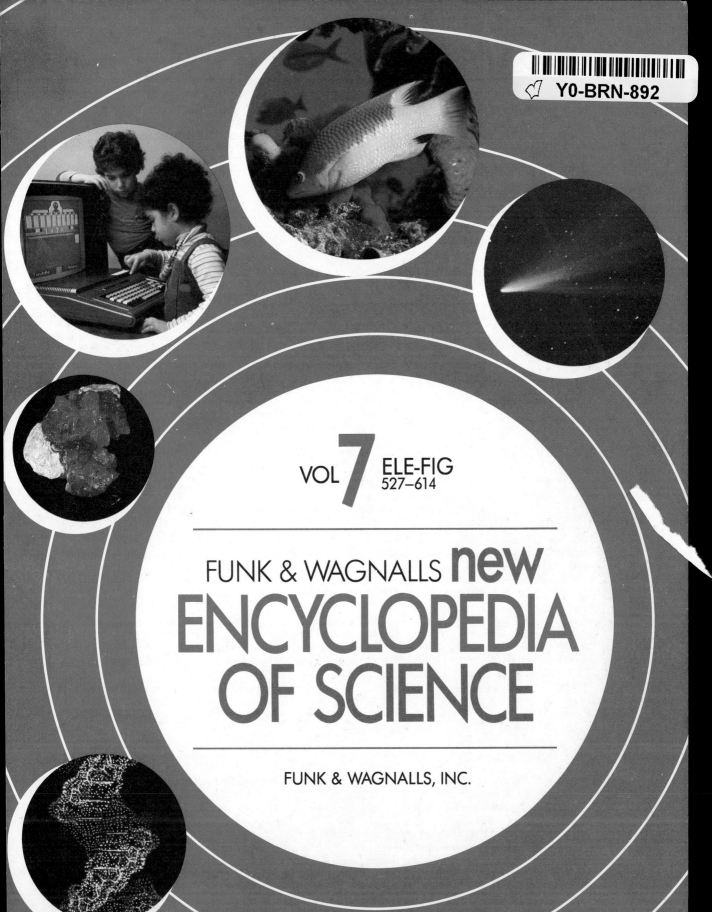

YO-BRN-892

VOL **7** ELE-FIG
527–614

FUNK & WAGNALLS **new**
ENCYCLOPEDIA
OF SCIENCE

FUNK & WAGNALLS, INC.

HOW TO USE FUNK & WAGNALLS NEW ENCYCLOPEDIA OF SCIENCE

Volumes 1 through 21 have information printed on the front covers, spine, and title pages that make it easy to find the articles you want to read.
- Volume numbers are printed in all three places in Volumes 1 through 21.
- Letter breaks — $\frac{COL}{DIA}$ — are printed in all three places in Volumes 1 through 21. The letters above the line are the first three letters of the first article title in the volume. The letters below the line are the first three letters of the last article title in the volume.
- Page breaks — $\frac{351}{438}$ — are printed on the spines and title pages of Volumes 1 through 21. They provide the page numbers of the first and last text pages in the volume.

Articles are arranged alphabetically by title in Volumes 1 through 21. Most titles are printed in **BOLD-FACE CAPITAL** letters. Some titles are printed in even larger letters.
- Some titles are not article titles, but refer you to the actual article title. Within articles you will find *See* or *See also* other article names for further information. All of these references to other articles are called cross-references.
- Most article titles are followed by a phonetic pronunciation. Use the Pronunciation Guide on page vi of Volume 1 to learn the correct pronunciation of the article title.
- At the end of most articles are two sets of initials. The first set identifies the person who wrote the article. The second set identifies the special consultant who checked the article for accuracy. All of these people are listed by their initials and full names and position on pages v and vi of Volume 1.
- ◼ This symbol at the end of an article indicates that there is a project based on the subject of the article in the Projects, Bibliography & Index volume. The project is found under its article title, and all of the project article titles are arranged alphabetically on pages 1 through 64 of the Projects, Bibliography & Index volume.

The Projects, Bibliography & Index Volume contains three sections. Each is an essential part of the encyclopedia.
- Projects based on articles in the encyclopedia are found in the first section. Each is both entertaining and educational. Each is designed for use by a student and for parental participation if desired.
- Bibliography reading lists in the second section list books under general scientific categories that are also titles of major articles. Each book listed is marked with either a YA (Young Adult) or J (Juvenile) reading level indicator. YA generally applies to readers at the junior high level or higher. J applies to readers at grade levels below junior high school.
- Index entries for all article titles plus many subjects that are not article titles are found in the third section. Instructions on using the Index are found at the start of the Index section in the Projects, Bibliography & Index volume.

ELECTROLYSIS (i lek′ träl′ ə səs) Electrolysis is the use of electricity to split up a substance into its different parts. Electrolysis can be used to extract metals from their ores. It can be used to purify metals. It can be used to prepare gases from liquids. Electrolysis is also used to put a layer of one metal closely on top of another. This is called electroplating.

Electrolysis only works with substances that can be dissolved or melted, and that will conduct an electric current. Substances that have these properties are called electrolytes.

When an electrolyte is melted or dissolved in water, its atoms or groups of atoms form ions. Ions are particles that bear electric charges. If the charges are positive, the ions are called cations. If they are negative charges, the ions are called anions. It is because they are electrically charged that ions can carry an electrical current through a solution. (*See* SOLUTION AND SOLUBILITY.) Hydrochloric acid is an electrolyte. It forms hydrogen ions with a positive charge, and chloride ions with a negative charge.

To electrolyze a substance, two electrodes are used. One is connected to the positive side of a battery or a DC electrical generator. The other is connected to the negative side. When the electrodes are dipped into the solution, the ions immediately start moving. The cations in the solution are attracted to the negative electrode (the cathode). The anions, with a negative charge, are attracted to the positive electrode (the anode).

When hydrochloric acid is electrolyzed, the hydrogen ions travel to the cathode, and the chloride ions travel to the anode. When the ions reach the electrodes, their electric charges are neutralized. The hydrogen ions become molecules of hydrogen gas, and the chloride ions become molecules of chlorine gas. Bubbles of the two different gases rise up from the electrodes.

When sodium chloride (common salt) is melted, it too can be electrolyzed. The result in this case is metallic sodium and chlorine gas. The sodium appears at the cathode, and chlorine bubbles up from the anode.

When a solution of sodium chloride is electrolyzed, the result is different. At the cathode, the sodium is released, but immediately it reacts with the water in the solution. This makes hydrogen gas and sodium hydroxide solution. At the anode, chlorine gas bubbles up as before.

Pure gases such as hydrogen, chlorine, and oxygen can easily be prepared by electrolysis. Pure metals such as sodium, potassium, and aluminum are also prepared in this way. Electrolysis is also a useful means of purifying, or refining, metals. Copper can be purified by using impure copper as the anode, and pure copper as the cathode. The electrolyte used is copper sulfate.

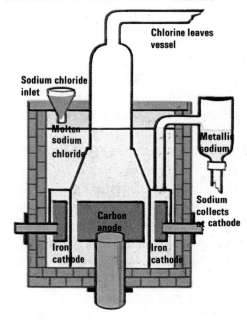

ELECTROLYSIS OF MOLTEN SODIUM CHLORIDE

Chlorine leaves vessel

Sodium chloride inlet

Molten sodium chloride

Metallic sodium

Sodium collects at cathode

Carbon anode

Iron cathode

Iron cathode

The diagrammatic cross section above shows the Downs cell. Molten, dry sodium chloride (salt) is split up into the elements sodium and chloride by passing an electric current through it. Sodium collects at the cathode and chlorine gas bubbles off at the anode. This reaction takes place on a commercial scale in the Downs cell.

ELECTROLYSIS OF IMPURE COPPER

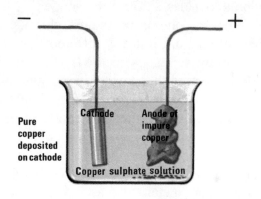

Pure copper deposited on cathode

Cathode

Anode of impure copper

Copper sulphate solution

Electrolysis is used to refine copper. The cathode consists of a block of pure copper. A piece of impure copper forms the anode. The electrolyte is copper sulphate solution. The action of the current splits the electrolyte into copper and sulphate ions. The copper ions go to the cathode. Meanwhile, copper atoms in the anode become copper ions and move into the electrolyte to make up for the copper ions moving to the cathode. The impurities in the anode remain behind. Overall, pure copper is dissolved from the anode and built up on the cathode.

Electrolysis is often carried out in a special container. The container is called an electrolytic cell. The cell must be made of material that is strong enough to resist the attack of hot liquids. The temperatures reached in electrolysis are often very high. The electrolyte, and the substances that are made from it, may be very corrosive substances. The electrodes must also be made of special material. If they were not, they would be eaten away when they were dipped into the electrolyte. Sometimes expensive metals like platinum are used to make electrodes. Carbon rods may also be used.

The electrodes do not need to be two rods. One electrode is sometimes the lining of the electrolytic cell. In the special cell to make sodium hydroxide from sodium chloride solution, one electrode is a layer of mercury forming the floor of the cell. The sodium dissolves in the mercury. It forms an amalgam. From the amalgam, sodium hydroxide can be extracted later.

In 1832, the British scientist Michael Faraday stated two laws about electrolysis. The first law says that the amount of a substance that forms at an electrode is proportional to the quantity of electricity that is passed through the electrolytic cell. The second law says that when the same amount of electricity is passed through different electrolytes, the amounts of different substances that are formed are proportional to their equivalent weights.   D.W./A.D.

ELECTROMAGNETIC RADIATION

(i lek′ trō mag net′ ik rād′ ē ā′ shən) There are many different kinds of electromagnetic radiation. Two very important kinds are light and radio waves. We need light to see things by. We use radio waves to send messages and for broadcasting. There are also other types of electromagnetic radiation. In fact, there is a complete range. The range is called the electromagnetic spectrum. The radiation with the most energy is called gamma rays. Then come X rays and ultraviolet rays. Next comes light, then infrared rays. The radiation with the least energy consists of microwaves and radio waves.

All electromagnetic radiation is made up of waves. They are produced by electrically charged particles. An electron is such a particle. These particles have an electric field. They move very fast. Because of this, they also have a magnetic field. (*See* ELECTROMAGNETISM.) Sometimes their speeds change. They are accelerated. Then their fields change as well. The particles move to and fro. They are said to vibrate. These vibrations form a wave. The wave moves away from the particles.

The fields vibrate at right angles to the direction of the wave. Therefore the waves are called transverse waves. The fields also vibrate at right angles to each other.

Some waves, like sound, need some material, like the air, to move in. The material is called the medium. Electromagnetic radiation

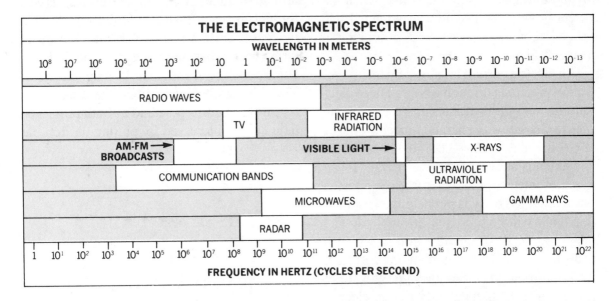

Electromagnetic radiation is the transmission of energy in the form of waves. These waves of energy can be grouped according to their wavelength or frequency into a continuous arrangement called a spectrum (above). Wavelength is the distance between the start of one wave and the start of the next. It is measured in meters in this diagram. Frequency is the number of times that a wave repeats itself in a second. One repetition is called a cycle. Frequency is measured in hertz, after the German scientist Heinrich Hertz. One hertz equals one cycle per second. The many different kinds of electromagnetic radiation, such as X rays, visible light, radio waves, and microwaves, all have different frequencies. Radio waves have frequencies of up to about a million million (10^{12}) hertz. The frequencies of the visible part of the spectrum are much greater than those of radio waves. Visible light has frequencies of about a million billion (10^{15}) hertz. The frequencies of X rays, gamma rays, and cosmic rays are even higher than those of light. X rays have frequencies of about a billion billion (10^{18}) hertz.

does not need any medium. It can travel in a vacuum. It moves faster in a vacuum than in any medium. In a vacuum, its speed is 299,790 km [186,281 mi] per second. This is called "the speed of light."

Discovery of electromagnetic waves   The existence of electromagnetic waves was first suggested by a Scottish mathematician in 1873. His name was James Clerk Maxwell. He also predicted radio waves. These waves were generated electrically by a German physicist, Heinrich Hertz. Ten years later X rays and gamma rays were discovered. They were being given off by radioactive atoms. (*See* RADIOACTIVITY.) Soon they were shown to be electromagnetic radiation. Early in this century the quantum theory was worked out. It explains electromagnetic radiation very well. Now we know that all electromagnetic radiation is given off in "packets." These packets are packets of energy. They are called quanta. Electromagnetic radiation is also absorbed in quanta.   M.E./J.T.

ELECTROMAGNETISM

The word electromagnetism (i lek' trō mag' nə tiz' əm) means two things. It is the magnetism produced by an electric current. It is also a branch of physics that studies the connections between electricity and magnetism. The study of electromagnetism began in the early 19th century. A Danish scientist named Hans Christian Oersted placed a magnetic needle near a wire that had a current flowing through it. He noticed that when the current flowed, the needle was deflected. He realized that the current was producing a magnetic field.

An electric current is caused by the movement of electrons through a wire. These electrons are very tiny particles and they have an electric charge. Any charged object produces an electric field. (*See* ELECTROSTATICS.) This field extends outward from the charge. It can be represented by lines of force. Suppose a second charged body is put near the first one. This body will be attracted or repelled. The lines of force show the direction in which it tends to move. For a wire with a current passing through it, these lines go outward at right angles. A charged body has an electric field around it whether the charges are moving or not. But if the charges are moving, then the body also has a magnetic field. Magnetism is always caused by moving electric charges. A current is caused by electrons flowing through the wire. Because these electrons are moving, they set up a magnetic field around the wire. The magnetic field can also be represented by lines of force. These lines form rings around the wire.

This can be shown very easily. Suppose you have a single strand of wire passing through a card. The wire and the card are at right angles. Some iron filings are scattered on the card. Iron filings are very small pieces of iron. A current is then passed through the wire. Iron is magnetic and tends to line up with a magnetic field. So the iron filings form rings around the wire. They have arranged themselves along the lines of force of the magnetic field. This shows the shape of the magnetic field around the wire. The strength of the field increases as the current in the wire gets stronger. It also varies with the distance from the wire. The further away the field, the weaker it gets.

A strong magnetic field can be made by passing a current through a solenoid. A solenoid is a long coil of insulated wire wound around a tube. When a current is passed through it, each turn of the coil produces a magnetic field. A solenoid usually has many turns, each producing a magnetic field. These fields combine to form a large magnetic field. The solenoid behaves rather like a bar magnet. It has a north pole and a south pole. The field can be increased by putting an iron bar

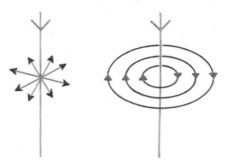

When an electric current is passed through a straight conductor, radial lines (left) of electrical force and circular lines (right) of magnetic force are set up at the same time around the straight conductor.

inside the solenoid. The iron becomes magnetized. Its field combines with the field caused by the current to form an even larger field. A solenoid with an iron bar inside it is known as an electromagnet. The first electromagnet was built in England in 1825 by William Sturgeon.

Electromagnets are very powerful. Since they have a magnetic field, they can be used to lift heavy iron and steel objects. An early electromagnet was built by Joseph Henry for the College of New Jersey (now Princeton University). It could lift 350 kg [770 lbs].

Large electromagnets produce a great amount of heat and they have to be kept cool. To do this, pipes carrying cold water are placed in the coil. In some electromagnets, the coil is made of hollow wires through which water can flow. The National Magnet Laboratory at the Massachusetts Institute of Technology has a very large electromagnet. It uses 16 million watts of electric power and needs 7,571 l [2,000 gal] of water every minute to keep it cool.

Electromagnetism is also concerned with using a magnetic field to make an electric current. This can be done by moving a piece of wire in a magnetic field. Moving the wire causes a current to flow in it. The current is said to be induced. (*See* INDUCTION.)

Uses of electromagnetism A country's electricity supply is produced by generators. These generators use mechanical power to produce electricity. A coil of wire is spun between the poles of a magnet. This induces a current in the wire. Sometimes the magnet is spun around the coil. An electromagnet can be used to magnetize steel. The iron inside a solenoid becomes magnetized when the solenoid is switched on. When it is switched off, the iron loses its magnetism. If a steel bar is put inside a solenoid, it too becomes magnetized. But when the current in the solenoid is switched off, the steel keeps some of its magnetism. Permanent magnets can be made in this way.

Powerful electromagnets are used in industry to lift iron and steel. They are also used for separating iron and steel from nonmagnetic metals like copper and brass. These metals are not attracted to a magnet.

The loudspeaker in a radio contains an electromagnet. It converts the electric signal into a mechanical force. This force is then used to produce sounds. In tape recorders, the tape is magnetized by a small electromagnet.

Particle accelerators are very large machines used in nuclear physics research. These accelerators use large electromagnets to make subatomic particles travel very fast. (*See* ACCELERATOR, PARTICLE.) There is an accelerator at Berkeley, California. Its electromagnet weighs over 4,000 tons. Its coil contains about 300 tons of copper.

Scientists are trying to use nuclear fusion to produce energy. The temperatures reached during fusion are very high indeed. They are so high that no substance can possibly withstand them. This means that the reacting gases cannot yet be confined. Scientists are looking at ways of using an electromagnetic field to do this. If the gases could be confined, then the fusion reaction could be controlled. Fusion reactors would supply almost limitless energy and solve the problem of the shortage of fuel.

M.E./A.I.

ELECTROMOTIVE FORCE (i lek′ trə mōt′ iv fōrs′) An electric circuit always contains a device that makes the charges move. This device provides the power for the circuit and is said to have an electromotive force. Electromotive force is usually shortened to EMF. Its strength is measured in volts. (*See* VOLTAGE.) The most common devices for providing an EMF are the electric cell and the generator. In an electric cell, an EMF is produced by chemical action. In a generator, electromagnetism is used to produce an EMF. Sometimes other methods are used. For example, heat can be used to produce an EMF. This can be done by putting a thermocouple into a circuit. If one of its junctions is heated, a current flows. Many kinds of photoelectric devices give an EMF when light shines on them. (*See* PHOTOELECTRIC EFFECT.) Another device that can be used is the fuel cell. Like the electric cell, it uses chemical action to produce an EMF. It may someday be used to power electric cars. M.E./J.T.

ELECTROMOTIVE SERIES (i lek′ trə mōt′ iv sir′ ēz) The electromotive series is a list of metals that shows how reactive they are. At the top of the list are the most reactive metals. Potassium is the first, followed by sodium. These are so reactive that they will even burst into flame when put into water. They are nearly always found as salts.

At the bottom of the list are the metals that react least with other substances. Platinum and gold will not even react with strong acids. Metals low on the list do not corrode readily. (*See* CORROSION.)

A metal high on the list will throw out, or

displace, a metal lower on the list from its salts. For example, iron is higher in the series than copper. So, if a piece of iron is dipped into a solution of copper sulfate, the copper is displaced. It forms a coating on the iron. At the same time, the iron turns into iron sulfate and dissolves.

The electromotive series is useful for predicting when two metals put close together will undergo corrosion. For example, if a nut is made from an element high in the series, and it is used with a bolt made from a metal much lower in the series, this is bad. After a while, corrosion will occur. The nut will gradually be eaten away. Engineers are always careful when they must use two metals together.

The electromotive series is also useful for telling how two different metals will act if they are used as the plates of a battery. The metal higher in the series always becomes the negative pole of the battery, while the lower metal becomes positive. The voltage that a battery produces depends upon the distance between the metals in the series. The greater the distance, the higher the voltage. *See also* REACTION, PRINCIPLE OF. D.W./A.D.

ELECTRON (i lek′ trän′) An electron is a subatomic particle that has a negative electric charge. An electron has an extremely small mass. It has about 1/1836 the mass of a hydrogen atom.

The atoms of all elements contain electrons. The negative charge of the electron is balanced by an equal number of positively-charged protons in the atom. The protons are in the nucleus of the atom, and the electrons orbit around them. Each chemical element requires a specific number of electrons and protons in order to remain neutral. This number is called the atomic number of the element.

We have used our knowledge of electrons to make many devices. Electric current is actually the flow of electrons through a wire.

An electron microscope works using a beam of electrons. The electron was discovered by the British physicist Sir J. J. Thomson, in 1897. J.M.C./A.D.

ELECTRONIC MUSIC (i lek′ trän′ ik myü′zik) Electronic music is made up of sounds that are produced by special electronic equipment, not by the musical instruments we usually hear in live performances or on records and tapes.

The basic unit of the special equipment is usually an oscillator. It produces sounds within the range of human hearing when its signal is sent through an amplifier and played back to the listener through a loudspeaker or headphones. More complicated instruments can be constructed by using many oscillators that produce a variety of sounds. These sounds can imitate those of traditional musical instruments, or they can be new and different from the usual musical sounds.

Musicians have different opinions about the uses of electronic music. A composer can write down the ''notes'' that he wants the electronic devices to produce. He has a wide choice of sounds that can be varied in pitch, loudness, duration, and other musical characteristics. He can even make electronic ''noise'' if his composition requires it. He can put the sounds of his composition together using a computer, or with a special device called a synthesizer. Whenever the composition is played for the listener, it will be exactly the same. It cannot be changed from one performance to the next by different musicians.

On the other hand, the musician can use his electronic instruments to experiment with musical sounds. He can mix the sounds in many different ways using a synthesizer. He can play someone else's composition, but change the sounds of the notes to suit himself. He can improvise and make new sounds as he plays along. He can conduct experiments with listeners to find out which sounds the listeners prefer and in which arrangements. He can add

This electronic synthesizer can create sounds that resemble those of musical instruments or the human voice.

or subtract parts of the sound to determine when the listener can just notice that the sound has changed.

In the sound laboratory or in the concert hall, the field of electronics has made possible the study of musical sounds from many different points of view. P.G.C./L.L.R.

ELECTRONICS (i lek′ trän′ iks) Electronics is a vital part of our daily lives. Cheap electronic equipment means that almost every home in richer countries has a television set. Radios are common in most parts of the world. Without electronic hearing aids, many deaf people would hear nothing. People with heart diseases use electronic devices called pacemakers to keep their hearts beating. Without them, the people would die. Electronic equipment such as X ray machines are widely used in hospitals.

History of electronics The science of electronics is about a hundred years old. An important piece of equipment in the history of electronics is the cathode-ray tube. This is a glass tube that has two electrodes in it. These electrodes can be joined into an electric circuit. When it is switched on, the current flows from one electrode to the other. There is only a very small amount of air inside the tube. If there were too much air inside, the molecules of the air would stop the flow of current.

The first discovery in electronics was made by Sir William Crookes in 1879. He showed that when a current flows in the cathode-ray tube, the negative electrode gives off rays. He called them cathode rays, since the negative electrode is called the cathode. In 1897, Sir J. J. Thomson discovered the electron. He also discovered that cathode rays were streams of electrons.

The next important step came in 1883. The American scientist, Thomas Edison, put a metal plate inside a light bulb. The plate was positively charged. When the light bulb was switched on, the filament glowed as usual. But Edison found that electricity was flowing from the filament to the metal plate. This is called thermionic emission. John Fleming put this effect to practical use. In 1904, he used the effect to build the first vacuum tube. It is called the diode because it has two electrodes. Three years later, Lee de Forest invented a different kind of vacuum tube, called a triode. A triode has a metal grid between the two electrodes. The grid is used to vary the strength of the electric current between the two electrodes. By this means, it amplifies, or makes stronger, the electric current and power. (*See* AMPLIFIER.) The diode and triode were used in the development of radio sets and telephones.

Two other vacuum tube devices are the magnetron and the klystron. They were invented in 1939 and were quickly used in the invention of radar. Radar is used to detect objects and find out how far away they are. It sends out radio waves. If the waves hit an object, they are reflected back. The radar set picks up these reflected waves and so detects the object. Radar can only detect objects above a certain size. If the radio waves have shorter wavelengths, then smaller objects can be detected. Magnetrons and klystrons pro-

Circuits being tested at the rate of 30 a minute in an electronics factory are shown above.

duce radio waves with very short wavelengths.

Meanwhile, the cathode ray tube was being improved. In 1926, John Logie Baird used it in his invention of the television. Later they were used in other electronic devices.

Modern electronics A major breakthrough in electronics occurred in 1947 when William Shockley invented the transistor. This tiny device can do everything a vacuum tube could do. It is both a rectifier (changing alternating current to direct current) and an amplifier. Transistors have many advantages. They weigh less than an ounce and take up very little space. They are sturdy and durable. And they use very little power to do their work.

The first transistors were made of crystals of germanium, a metallic element. Then it was found that silicon could serve as well as germanium. This was fortunate because silicon is so plentiful. It exists in nature as silicon dioxide, ordinary sand. Using silicon, laboratories could make thousands of transistors quickly and inexpensively. This was important because in the 1950s and 1960s the U. S. Government's space program needed thousands of transistors. So did the computer industry. Transistors also were used in radios, record players, television sets, hearing aids, and many other devices.

The availability of the transistor put in motion a dramatic shift toward miniaturization of electronic devices. This started in the mid-1960s when several laboratories developed the integrated electronic circuit. This device consists of a single miniaturized silicon component that combines the functions of several individual components. Among these individual components are interconnected transistors. This accomplishment was only the beginning. Before the end of the decade, large-scale integration (LSI) had emerged. Techniques were soon found whereby hundreds and even thousands of electronic circuits could be put on a single silicon wafer, or chip, about the size of a quarter.

To produce these miniature marvels, engineers first make a drawing of the electronic circuitry on mylar sheets several hundred times the size of the final product. These sheets are later reduced in size photographically. They are then printed on chemically treated silicon chips and further processed. The finished product is a true miniature of the original drawing. Some of these chips can pass throught the eye of a needle with room to spare.

Application of the integrated circuit to computer design pointed the way toward miniaturization of computers. The room-sized monsters of the early days gave way to less cumbersome transistorized models. The use of integrated circuits gave rise to still smaller desk-top models called minicomputers. But when Marcian E. (Ted) Hoff, Jr. came up with a new concept for the design of LSI chips in 1969, unbelievably small computers became a possibility. He condensed all of the computer's arithmetic so it could fit on just one chip. This silicon chip, called a microprocessor, was a boon to the computer industry. It is the heart of the small computer. Because of this invention, home computers, video games, and pocket calculators became

These devices are called programmable controllers. They are industrial computers that can be programmed to perform a series of commands to operate various machines and processes.

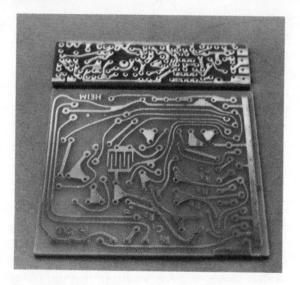

An enlarged gold-plated printed circuit, for use in equipment such as televisions, is pictured above.

a reality. The applications of Hoff's invention are endless.

Hooking his microprocessor to a data chip and a control chip gave Hoff his microcomputer. It was about the size of a jelly bean. It could perform 10,000 calculations per second. That performance equals what the monstrous ENIAC could do with its 18,000 vacuum tubes. A big advantage of the microcomputer is its flexibility. Changing its memory chip changes its program.

This space-saving computer is invaluable to space technology. The success of the totally computerized space shuttle *Columbia* makes this point. National defense and military and civil aviation also use this device. Thousands of automated industrial and business operations will be able to cut costs through its use. M.E./L.L.R.

ELECTRON MICROSCOPE (i lek′ trän′ mī′ krə skōp′) An electron microscope is a microscope that can magnify objects over a half million times. (*See* MAGNIFICATION.) An electron microscope works on a principle similar to that of a regular light microscope. In a light microscope, a bright light is directed through a specimen (object to be magnified) and into the microscope's objective lens. The light rays are focused by the lens, producing a magnified image. (*See* LENS.)

In an electron microscope, a beam of fast-moving electrons is passed through a very thin slice of the specimen. The electrons are focused by magnetic lenses onto a fluorescent screen. (*See* FLUORESCENCE.) On the screen, the magnified image can be observed directly or photographed.

Scanning electron microscope   A scanning electron microscope works in the same way as a television camera. (*See* TELEVISION.) A scanning electron microscope scans the surface of a specimen with a fine beam of electrons. A picture is obtained that shows detail of the specimen's surface.

Through the use of electron microscopes,

A scanning electron microscope moves a beam of electrons across a specimen. The electrons then pass through a collector and the magnified image is formed on a television screen such as the one shown above.

scientists have obtained much new knowledge about viruses, bacteria, and other microscopic forms of life. The scientists who work with electron microscopes are called electron microscopists. Electron microscopes are found in many hospitals, universities, and laboratories. *See also* ELECTRON.

J.M.C./S.S.B.

Photographs taken by means of electron microscopes are known as electron micrographs. Shown above are two examples of micrographs, taken with the type of electron microscope that scans the object in the way that a television camera scans a scene. The micrographs show the contrast in structure between natural and synthetic fibers. Left, a fiber of wool; right, a nonwoven fabric made of Heterofil fibers, showing the detail of the bond between the fibers.

ELECTRON VOLT (i lek′ trän′ vōlt′) An electron volt is a measurement of nuclear energy. It is the energy gained by an electron when it passes from one point to another point that is one volt higher in potential. One electron volt is equal to approximately 1.6×10^{-19} joules. The burning of one atom of carbon in coal or oil produces about three electron volts of energy. The fissioning of one uranium nucleus produces about 200 million electron volts. (*See* FISSION.)   W.R.P./J.T.

ELECTROPHORESIS (i lek′ trə fə rē′ səs) Electrophoresis is a method sometimes used to separate the particles of different substances in a solution. (*See* SOLUTION AND SOLUBILITY.) An electric current is passed through the solution from one electrode to another. Many substances are made of particles that have an electric charge. When the electric current passes, the particles are attracted to one of the electrodes. They gradually move through the solution.

The speed at which the particles move depends upon how big they are, and what size of electric charge they have. By switching off the current after a certain time, it is possible to separate different particles in a solution. Modern methods of electrophoresis use wet filter paper or plates of gelatine instead of a container of water.

Electrophoresis has been used to separate the different proteins in the blood. It has been used to detect disease. It can be used to detect the presence of drugs and poisons in the body.

D.M.H.W./A.D.

ELECTROPLATING (i lek′ trə plāt′ ing) Electroplating is a method of coating an article with a thin layer of metal. Usually the article itself is also made of metal. When an article is coated with a metal, it is said to be plated. In electroplating, the coating is done by electrolysis.

In electrolysis, two electrodes are placed in a liquid. A current is then passed through the liquid from one electrode to the other. In electroplating, the article and the metal that forms the coating are used as electrodes. They are placed in a solution of a compound of the metal. (*See* SOLUTION AND SOLUBILITY.) Usually this compound is a salt. The article and the metal are then connected to a supply of DC electricity. The positive side of the supply is attached to the metal and the negative side to the article. The current flows from the metal, through the solution, to the article. As the current flows, the metal electrode is gradually "eaten away." The metal goes into the solution and comes out of the solution onto the article.

For example, suppose you want to coat a brass faucet with nickel. The faucet and the

The metal parts (left) will be plated with zinc in this programmed, automated electroplating system.

nickel would be used as electrodes. Usually a salt of nickel called nickel sulfate is used as the solution. When the current is switched on, the faucet gradually becomes coated with brilliant nickel plate.

Electroplating was first done about a hundred years ago. The first metal to be used for coating was silver. A cheap metal could be coated and made to look as if it were made out of silver. Spoons, forks, and other articles were coated in this way. Silver-plated articles look as if they were made of solid silver. But, of course, they are much cheaper to produce. Such articles are stamped with the letters E.P.N.S. This stands for Electroplated Nickel Silver. If they were not stamped, people might think that they were solid silver.

Articles are often plated with chromium. Chromium is much harder than other metals and also prevents rusting. Therefore, chromium-plated articles last longer. Automobile bumpers are made out of steel. They are then plated with copper, followed by nickel, and then by chromium.

The thickness of the coating varies. It depends on the article to be coated and on the metal used. In silver plating, the coating is only 1/2000 mm [0.00002 in]. A recent development in electroplating is called "hard chromium" plating. Here, a much thicker layer of chromium is used than would be normal. It is about 1/50 mm [0.0008 in] thick. This process is used to restore machine parts. It is also used to plate the tips of tools, such as drills. It makes them last longer.

Materials other than metals can also be electroplated. Most other materials do not conduct electricity. They have to be coated with a thin layer of graphite first. Graphite is a form of carbon and conducts electricity. This method is sometimes used to coat plaster casts with copper.   M.E./A.D.

Above, the gold-leaf electroscope.

ELECTROSCOPE (i lek′ trə skōp′) The electroscope is an instrument used to detect electric charge. (*See* CHARGE, ELECTRIC.) The electroscope can also be used to tell whether the charge is positive or negative. Electroscopes can also detect X rays and other electromagnetic radiation.

The gold-leaf electroscope is a common type of electroscope. In 1787, Abraham Bennet, a British scientist, invented the gold-leaf electroscope. The instrument consists of two slender strips of gold foil hanging from a metal rod. The metal rod acts as a conductor. (*See* CONDUCTION OF ELECTRICITY.) A nonconductor, such as wood, holds the conductor in a stand. The stand is often made of glass.

When the conductor has no electric charge, the foil strips hang straight down. If the conductor is charged with electricity, the strips become charged. Both strips receive the same kind of charge. Because bodies with like charges repel each other, the strips move apart. The amount of movement gives an indication of the strength of the charge. The electroscope can be used to measure high voltages. William Henly, a British scientist, converted an electroscope into an electrometer by adding a scale of numbers to it. An elec-

trometer measures the strength of electric charges.

To find out whether a charge is positive or negative, the activated electroscope is tested with a known charge. For example, if a known positive charge makes the foil strips fall back together, the unknown charge is negative. Opposite charges neutralize each other. If the strips spread further apart, the unknown charge is positive. *See also* ELECTROSTATICS.   J.J.A./J.T.

ELECTROSTATICS (i lek′ trə stat′ iks) Electric charges can be either moving or still. For example, in an electric circuit the charges are moving in the wire. If an object is rubbed, it sometimes gains an electric charge. In this case the charges are not moving. They are said to be static. The electricity is called static electricity. The study of static electricity is called electrostatics.

When materials like amber are rubbed, they are able to attract light objects such as feathers. The ancient Greeks knew this. In the 1500s, William Gilbert found that many other materials behaved in the same way when rubbed. He called this effect electric, after the Greek word *elektron*, which means amber. He found, for example, that glass could be electrified by rubbing it with silk. However, he could not find a way to electrify metals. In 1729, Stephen Gray discovered another difference between metals and other materials. He found that electricity can flow along metals but not along nonmetals. Metals are said to conduct electricity and are called conductors. Conductors other than metals have been discovered since then. One such conductor is graphite. Materials in which electricity does not flow are called insulators.

A very important discovery was made in France around 1733 by the scientist Charles DuFay. He found that there are two different kinds of electric charge. They are called positive charge and negative charge. He found that bodies having the same kind of charge

Lightning results from a great natural build-up of static electricity. 1. An electrical charge (usually negative) accumulates on the underside of a thundercloud. Attracted by this negative charge, a positive electrical charge accumulates on high objects beneath the cloud. 2 and 3. As the build-up of electrostatic charges goes on, "leader streams"

of electric current are sent down from the cloud, and up from high points on the ground. 4. Finally, the electrical resistance of the air between the ground and the cloud is broken down. At this point, a flash of lightning is seen bridging the gap between cloud and ground. The cloud has momentarily lost its electric charge as this happens.

repelled, or pushed each other away. Bodies with opposite charges attracted each other. In both cases, there is a force acting between the two bodies. The English scientist Joseph Priestley studied this force. He found that for spherical objects the strength of the force depends on the distance between the two bodies. He made this discovery in 1766. He showed that the electric force obeys the inverse square law. This law says that the force increases as the two bodies get closer together. If the distance between the two is halved, the force becomes four times as strong. (*See* INVERSE SQUARE LAW.)

In 1787, a very important instrument was invented. It is called the the gold-leaf electroscope and is used to detect electric charge. It was soon used to investigate the charge on a hollow body. The electroscope showed that all the charge lies on the outside surface. The inside surface has no charge at all.

Scientists still did not know what electricity was. They thought that it was like a liquid. We know now that many electric effects are caused by very small particles called electrons. Electrons are negatively charged and are found in atoms. An atom has a heavy core called a nucleus. Surrounding this core there are a number of electrons. When two materials are rubbed together, the electrons are sometimes pulled out of the atoms. They get transferred from one material to another. When glass is rubbed with silk, the electrons move from the glass to the silk. Since the electrons have a negative charge, the silk becomes negatively charged. The glass has lost electrons, so it gains a positive charge. Ebonite can become charged by being rubbed with fur. In this case, the electrons move from the fur to the ebonite. The ebonite becomes negatively charged and the fur positively charged.

The SI unit of electric charge is called the coulomb. It is the amount of electricity that a current of one ampere transfers in one second. (*See* INTERNATIONAL SYSTEM.)

The electric field If a body has a charge, it is said to be surrounded by an electric, or electrostatic, field. When another charged body is placed near the first body, it is affected by the field. The field produces a force on the body. The body is either attracted or repelled. A large charge sets up a strong electric field. The strength of the field varies from point to point. It is strongest nearest the body causing it. Further away, the field gets weaker.

A useful idea is to imagine the field as lines of force. These lines show the direction in which a positive charge would move in the field. For a round body, the lines of force of its field are straight lines. If its charge is positive, they go outward from the charge evenly in every direction. They go outward because a positive charge repels, or pushes away, another positive charge. If the charge is negative, the lines go in the opposite direction. They go inward to the charge. This shows that it attracts a positive charge. As the lines of force move away from the body, they spread out. The field also becomes weaker. Similarly, near the body the lines are close together and the field is strong. In other words the strength of the field is related to the density of the lines.

For a sphere that is a conductor, the charge is spread evenly over the surface. Suppose the charged body is not a sphere, but is shaped like a football. This shape is curved most at the ends. Most of the charges are gathered at the ends. This means that the electric field depends on the shape of the body causing it. The field is strongest where the body curves most. For a sphere, the electrostatic field has the same strength all around it. Its strength changes only as you move away from the sphere. For a body shaped like a football, the field is greatest at either end.

Electrostatic charging We have already come across one way of charging an object. This is by rubbing it with something. Not all objects can be charged like this, though.

Another way is by touching it with a charged body. A third method is called induction. With induction, no contact is made with another body.

Imagine two metal balls touching each other but insulated from everything else. They could be placed on the end of glass rods, for example. The rods could then be held in the hand and the balls would be insulated. An ebonite rod with a negative charge is then brought close to one of them. The ebonite repels the electrons in that ball and they move to the ball that is further away. This ball becomes negatively charged because the electrons have a negative charge. The ball near the rod has a positive charge because it has lost some electrons. They remain charged as long as the rod is held in place. When the rod is taken away, they lose their charges because the electrons flow back again. Suppose the rod is kept in place and the balls are separated. They stay charged because the rod is still there. But now, if the rod is removed, the electrons cannot flow back. There is no contact between the balls. The two balls have been charged by induction. One has a positive charge and the other a negative charge.

Electric charge can be stored in capacitors. These are made out of two conductors placed close together but not touching. Usually a capacitor has two pieces of metal foil separated by some insulating material. One way to charge a capacitor is by connecting it to a battery. The battery sets up a potential difference across the capacitor. This causes the pieces of foil in the capacitor to have opposite charges. These charges remain there when the battery is removed. M.E./A.I.

ELEMENT

Elements (el′ ə mənts) are the simple materials from which everything in the universe is made. An element is made of atoms. In any element there are only atoms of one kind. An element cannot be broken down into anything else but its own kind of atoms in a chemical reaction. There are over 100 different elements that occur in the universe. Some of them are very common. Carbon, for example, is found in every living animal and plant.

Elements can occur by themselves. A pure metal such as gold consists of only atoms of gold. It is an element. Pure hydrogen gas is another element that can exist by itself. In nature, however, elements are usually found linked to other elements. When two or more different elements are linked together they form a chemical compound. Water, for example, is a compound of the elements hydrogen and oxygen. Sodium chloride (common salt) is a compound of the two elements sodium and chlorine.

Elements can mix together without having to form a compound. Air is a mixture of the elements nitrogen, oxygen, and argon. It is not a compound, because the elements are not joined together chemically.

Kinds of elements   There are two ways of classifying elements. One way is to divide them into metals and non-metals. Metals make up more than three-quarters of all the elements. However, many of the non-metallic elements are abundant in nature. Oxygen, hydrogen, carbon, and silicon are very common non-metallic elements.

The other way of classifying elements is to divide them into solids, liquids, and gases at normal temperature and pressure. If this is done, most elements are found to be solids. Bromine and mercury are liquids. The elements oxygen and nitrogen are gases.

Chemical names and symbols   Every element has its own name and a chemical symbol. The name of the element often gives a clue to what sort of substance it is. Nearly all of the metallic elements have the ending -ium, for example. Some of the metals which have been known for a very long time do not end with -ium. Gold, zinc, iron, and nickel were in use long before the custom was adopted.

Most of the elements have names that come from Latin and Greek words. Hydrogen comes from the Greek for watermaker, because it can be burned to make water. Krypton comes from the Greek for concealed, because it was so hard to discover in the atmosphere. Bromine was named for the Greek for stench, because of its bad smell. Some elements are named for places or for scientists. Francium is named for France, and einsteinium, nobelium, and curium for the scientists Einstein, Nobel, and Curie.

The symbol of an element is a kind of shorthand for the name. The symbols are either one or two letters. Often the symbol comes from the English name. Thus O stands for oxygen and S for sulfur. It may come from the Latin name, like Na for sodium (natrium) and Ag for silver (argentum).

The abundance of the elements The most abundant element in the universe is the gaseous element hydrogen. The sun and the stars consist mostly of this element. In the earth's crust, the most abundant element is oxygen. Oxygen is found in the atmosphere, in the oceans as water, and in many minerals. Next most abundant is silicon. Silicon is found in nearly every rock found on earth, except for limestone.

Some elements are very rare. Radium is one example. It is one of the radioactive elements. Radioactive elements are rare because they gradually change into different elements. Radium eventually changes into the more common element lead. This kind of change is called radioactive decay. To obtain just one-tenth of a gram of radium, Marie and Pierre Curie had to work hard for many months. They had to extract it from several tons of the rocky ore called pitchblende.

Atomic structure All elements are made of atoms. It is the way that their atoms differ that makes every element different. To understand how one atom is different from another, it is necessary to understand what an atom is made of. Atoms are made of small particles. These are called subatomic particles. It is the number of particles that makes one atom different from another.

In the center of every atom is a group of particles. Some of them are protons. They have a positive electric charge. The rest are neutrons. They have no electric charge. Together these particles make up the nucleus of the atom. Outside the nucleus are electrons. These are particles with a negative electric charge. The number of electrons in an atom is the same as the number of protons. The positive and negative electric charges balance one another, so that each atom is electrically neutral.

The number of protons in the nucleus of an atom is called the atomic number. It is the same in all the atoms of one element. It identifies that element. Every atom with the atomic number 6 is a carbon atom, for example. The number of neutrons in the nucleus is not always the same. Atoms which have the same atomic number but different numbers of neutrons are called isotopes of the same element.

Orbital electrons Each atom has orbital electrons around its nucleus. The electrons move in what are called electron shells. The shells are arranged at different distances from the nucleus. Nearest to the nucleus is the first shell. The first shell may contain up to two electrons, but no more. Further out is the second shell. This may contain up to eight electrons. The third shell may contain up to 18 electrons.

The simplest element is hydrogen. It has the atomic number 1. In its nucleus is just one proton. It has one electron circling the nucleus, in the first shell. The element with

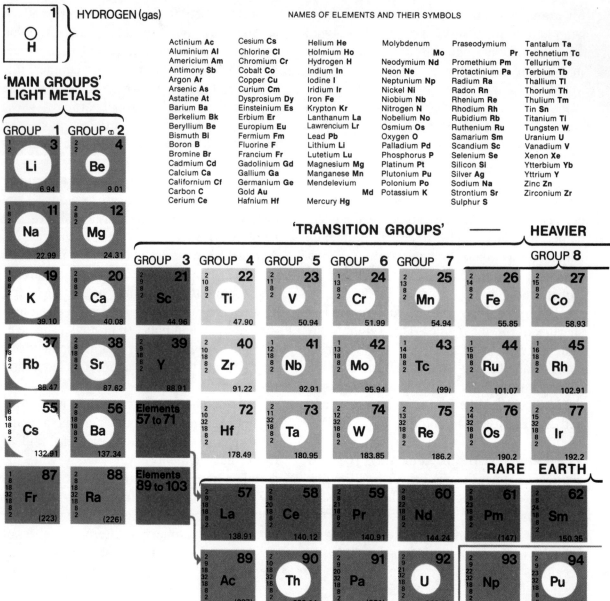

HYDROGEN (gas)

NAMES OF ELEMENTS AND THEIR SYMBOLS

Actinium Ac	Cesium Cs	Helium He	Molybdenum
Aluminium Al	Chlorine Cl	Holmium Ho	Mo
Americium Am	Chromium Cr	Hydrogen H	Neodymium Nd
Antimony Sb	Cobalt Co	Indium In	Neon Ne
Argon Ar	Copper Cu	Iodine I	Neptunium Np
Arsenic As	Curium Cm	Iridium Ir	Nickel Ni
Astatine At	Dysprosium Dy	Iron Fe	Niobium Nb
Barium Ba	Einsteinium Es	Krypton Kr	Nitrogen N
Berkelium Bk	Erbium Er	Lanthanum La	Nobelium No
Beryllium Be	Europium Eu	Lawrencium Lr	Osmium Os
Bismuth Bi	Fermium Fm	Lead Pb	Oxygen O
Boron B	Fluorine F	Lithium Li	Palladium Pd
Bromine Br	Francium Fr	Lutetium Lu	Phosphorus P
Cadmium Cd	Gadolinium Gd	Magnesium Mg	Platinum Pt
Calcium Ca	Gallium Ga	Manganese Mn	Plutonium Pu
Californium Cf	Germanium Ge	Mendelevium	Polonium Po
Carbon C	Gold Au	Md	Potassium K
Cerium Ce	Hafnium Hf	Mercury Hg	

Praseodymium	Tantalum Ta
Pr	Technetium Tc
Promethium Pm	Tellurium Te
Protactinium Pa	Terbium Tb
Radium Ra	Thallium Tl
Radon Rn	Thorium Th
Rhenium Re	Thulium Tm
Rhodium Rh	Tin Sn
Rubidium Rb	Titanium Ti
Ruthenium Ru	Tungsten W
Samarium Sm	Uranium U
Scandium Sc	Vanadium V
Selenium Se	Xenon Xe
Silicon Si	Ytterbium Yb
Silver Ag	Yttrium Y
Sodium Na	Zinc Zn
Strontium Sr	Zirconium Zr
Sulphur S	

atomic number 2 is helium. It has two protons in its nucleus. Around this, two electrons orbit. They fill up the first shell. Element number 3 is lithium. It has three protons in its nucleus, so it must have three electrons in orbit. Two of them are in the first shell, and the other one is in the second shell. As the atomic number of the element increases, the shells fill up. Element number 11 is sodium. It has two electrons in the first shell (full), eight in the second shell (full), and one in the third shell, making 11.

Properties of the elements The properties of the elements depend upon the arrangement of the electrons in their shells. This is because when atoms of elements react with others, electrons form bonds between them. Elements with full outer shells tend to be inert. They do not easily make compounds with

PERIODIC TABLE OF THE ELEMENTS

The elements in the same group (vertical column) of the periodic table are similar to each other, but their properties gradually change from one end of the group to the other.

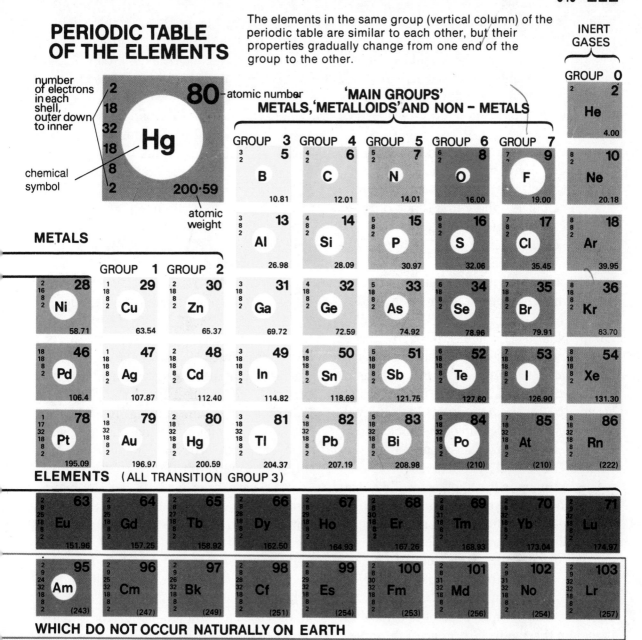

other elements. They do not have electrons to spare to link with other atoms. Helium, neon, and argon are elements with full outer shells. They do not react with other elements. They are three of the noble gases.

Elements with only a few electrons in their outer shells are more reactive. They form compounds readily with other elements. They may lend electrons to other elements, or they may share electrons with them. They may borrow electrons from other elements to fill their outer shells. These are all ways in which atoms may combine together to form compounds. (*See* VALENCE.)

The periodic table In 1869, the Russian chemist Dmitri Mendeleev drew a table of all the elements that were then known. He arranged them by their atomic weight. He showed that there was a pattern. Elements with the same sorts of properties occurred at regular intervals, or periods, in the table. Mendeleev's periodic table is still used today, but we now arrange the elements by atomic number, not atomic weight. We can add the many elements that had not been discovered in those days.

In the table atomic numbers increase from left to right. Hydrogen, element 1, starts the table at top left. Helium, element 2, is at top right. The others follow in a series of rows. The horizontal rows are called periods. The vertical columns are called groups. The groups are numbered.

The elements in any particular group have similar properties. There is a gradual change, however, from top to bottom of each group. Note that groups 1 through 7 occur twice, both as a main group and as a transition group. (Main groups are sometimes numbered 1a, 2a, 3a, etc., and transition groups 1b, 2b, 3b, etc.) Group 8 is not divided like this. Nor is group 0, the noble gases.

The elements of main group 1a are very similar. They are all soft, light, silver-colored metals. Lithium is the lightest metal known. It is at the top of the group. It is very reactive. Further down, the metals become more reactive. Sodium (Na) reacts violently with water, and catches fire. Potassium (K) almost explodes when it touches water. Rubidium (Rb) is so reactive that it catches fire when it even meets air. It must be kept in a vacuum. Francium (Fr), at the heavy end of the group, is radioactive.

Changes like these are seen in all the groups. In main group 4a, carbon (C) is a non-metal. At the other end, tin (Sn) and lead (Pb) are metals. Between are silicon (Si) and germanium (Ge). Elements that have some of the properties of metals and some of the properties of non-metals are called metalloids.

At the top of main group 6a is oxygen (O), which is a gas. Beneath it is sulfur (S), a non-metal solid. The other three elements are metalloids. Polonium (Po) is highly radioactive.

The properties of the elements show an orderly pattern through main groups 1a and 7a. However, the elements in groups 3a, 4a, and 5a do not show as much resemblance among themselves as the elements in groups 1a, 2a, 6a, and 7a. In group 0 are the inert gases. They are almost completely unreactive, and are similar in this way.

The elements in the transition groups 1b through 7b, and group 8, are all fairly heavy metals. In group 8, the metals in the same period (horizontal row) show strong similarities. Thus iron (Fe), cobalt (Co), and nickel (Ni) are very similar metals.

Elements that show a particularly great similarity are found in transition group 3b. Elements 57 through 71 belong to the rare earth group. (*See* RARE EARTH ELEMENTS.) These are all metals. They have such similar properties that they are very difficult to separate from one another. Elements 89 through 103 show the same strong resemblance. Those after uranium (U) are called transuranic elements. They are radioactive, and only one, plutonium (Pu), exists naturally. The rest have been made in the laboratory. (*See* ACCELERATORS.) Elements with atomic numbers up to 109 have been made this way.

Artificial elements Artificial elements can be made from natural elements. This is done by bombarding the natural elements with subatomic particles. An atomic reactor or particle accelerator is used. Some of the artificial elements are called the transuranic elements. They are all highly radioactive and dangerous. Some, like plutonium (Pu) last for millions of years. Others, like lawrencium (Lr) decay in a matter of seconds. *See also* ACCELERATOR, PARTICLE.   D.M.H.W./J.R.W.

ELEPHANT (el′ ə fənt) The elephant is the largest living land animal. These mammals belong to the order Proboscidea, referring to their large, useful trunks. Elephants have

Indian, or Asian, elephants are smaller, less fierce and easier to tame than their African cousins. Left, an Indian elephant, ridden by his *mahout,* or driver, carries a log. Trained elephants can carry loads of up to 600 pounds on their backs or with their trunks. They are particularly useful in forestry for carrying heavy logs.

fairly large brains, weighing about 5 kg [11 lb], small eyes, and large ears. Its tusks are made of ivory and are actually incisors from the upper jaw. (See TEETH.) An elephant's trunk may be 1.8 m [6 ft] long and weigh 140 kg [308 lb]. It is boneless, contains more than 40,000 muscles, and can lift objects as small as a peanut or as large as a log weighing 275 kg [605 lb]. The tip of the trunk is very sensitive, and, like a hand, can feel an object to determine its shape, texture, and temperature.

A wild elephant eats constantly, consuming as much as 275 kg [605 lb] of food per day. The elephant, a herbivore, uses its trunk to uproot trees and plants for food. An elephant drinks by sucking water into its trunk and squirting it into its mouth.

Elephants are sometimes called pachyderms (meaning ''thick-skinned'') because their skin is about 2.5 cm [1 in] thick and weighs about 950 kg [2090 lb]. In spite of the thickness of the skin, elephants are very sensitive to insect bites and will leave an otherwise favorable area to avoid insects. Since the elephant lacks a protective layer of fat under the skin, it is sensitive to very hot or very cold weather.

An elephant has large, round feet and legs which can measure 50 cm [20 in] in diameter. The feet spread out under its weight, but become smaller when lifted, keeping the elephant from getting stuck in mud or marshes. Though elephants walk at about 10 km [6 mi] per hour, a frightened elephant may run as fast as 40 km [25 mi] per hour.

A female elephant (cow) may be pregnant for 20 to 22 months before giving birth to a calf weighing about 90 kg [198 lb]. The calf nurses for three or four years, is sexually mature by age 14, and is fully grown by age 20. Most elephants live to be about 60 years old. Though many people believe that old elephants go to an ''elephant graveyard'' to die, this has never been proven.

Elephants are social animals, roaming in herds of 10 to 100 or more. The leader is usually a female. When elephants move from one area to another, they walk in a single file with the female leader followed by the other females, the calves, and finally, the males

Below, an African elephant with its calf. This elephant has a slow reproductive cycle, and conception to birth takes 21 months.

(bulls). If threatened, the bulls form a protective circle around the cows and calves. Adult elephants are rarely attacked by other animals, though they sometimes fight among themselves. Bulls try to gore each other with their tusks while cows try to bite off each other's tails. Rogue elephants are loners that will attack any animal or person they see. Rogues are usually old bulls that have been chased out of the herd by younger bulls. Their violent behavior is probably caused by pain from disease or decayed teeth.

There are two main species of elephants. The African elephant *(Loxodonta africana)* is dark gray, has two fingerlike structures on the tip of its trunk, and has huge ears (1.2 m [4 ft] wide). The African bull may be 3.5 m [11.5 ft] at the shoulder and weigh as much as 5,500 kg [12,100 lb]. Both bulls and cows have tusks which may be as long as 3.0 m [9.9 ft] and weigh as much as 65 kg [143 lb]. Generally, the female is smaller and has smaller tusks than the male. African elephants are found south of the Sahara Desert and north of South Africa.

The Asian (or Indian) elephant *(Elephas maximus)* is smaller and less fierce than the African elephant. It lives in India and southeast Asia. It has an arched back, two bumps on its forehead between the ears, and one fingerlike structure on the tip of its trunk. Its ears are also smaller, measuring about 0.6 m [2 ft] across. The bull stands about 2.7 m [9 ft] at the shoulder and weighs about 5,000 kg [11,000 lb]. Most Asian elephants are light gray, though some are white with pink eyes. The bull's tusks are about 1.5 m [5 ft] long, and the female's are much smaller. Some Asian elephants have no tusks at all.

Elephants have long been hunted for sport and for the valuable ivory of their tusks. Unlimited hunting has greatly reduced the numbers of elephants, and laws have been established, though rarely enforced, to protect them. In addition, refuges have been set up where hunters are not allowed to kill elephants. Unfortunately many thousands of elephants are killed illegally every year, and the wild elephant is rapidly becoming an endangered species in some areas. In other places, elephants are so numerous that control-hunting by game wardens is necessary to keep them from completely destroying the local habitat.   A.J.C./J.J.M.

ELEPHANT SEAL (el′ ə fənt sēl) The elephant seal *(Mirounga leonina)*, or sea

The elephant seal is the second largest sea mammal. Only the whale is larger.

elephant, is the largest of the seals. The male (bull) may reach a length of 6 m [20 ft] and a weight of 2750 kg [6050 lb]. The female (cow) is usually about half this size. This mammal gets its name from the fact that the bull has a large nose which hangs over its mouth. This nose can be inflated to form a trunklike snout 38 cm [15 in] long.

Every year, the bulls engage in intensive fighting to establish large groups of females as mates. A cow gives birth to one calf that nurses for several weeks before joining the adults in the daily hunts for food. These seals are carnivores, feeding on squids and fishes, some of which live several hundred meters deep in the ocean.

Elephant seals have been hunted for their skins and their blubber. The blubber from one elephant seal can yield as much as 950 kg [2090 lb] of oil. Until recently, the hunting was so extensive that the elephant seal was facing extinction. Only the total prohibition of seal hunting in certain areas has allowed this species to increase its numbers beyond the endangered level. Elephant seals are found in and near Antarctica. Some have been sighted as far north as the Pacific coast of the United States. A.J.C./J.J.M.

ELEPHANT SHREW (el' ə fənt shrü') The elephant shrew is any of 16 species of insect-eating mammals belonging to the family Macroscelididae. It is named for its long, flexible snout which is used to probe soil and leaf litter in search of insects. Elephant shrews vary in length from 17 to 57 cm [7 to 22 in]. They are usually yellowish in color, and have long hind legs which enable them to make great leaps if disturbed. They have large ears and eyes, and long thin tails. The elephant shrew hunts by day. It lives in dry, rocky areas of Africa. *See also* SHREW. A.J.C./J.J.M.

ELK (elk) An elk is one of two species belonging to the deer family. The American elk *(Cervus elaphus* or *Cervus canadensis)* is a brownish deer that was called *wapiti* by the American Indians. The male (bull) stands about 1.5 m [5 ft] tall at the shoulder and may weigh as much as 450 kg [990 lb]. Its antlers may spread more than 1.5 m [5 ft] and have 12 or more points. The female (cow) is smaller and does not have antlers.

American elk are herbivores and graze in large herds. They usually spend the winters in valleys where snowfall is light, returning to the mountains in the spring. Many elk die of starvation or disease in the winter. In the fall, bulls fight for mates and for leadership of the herd. Some bulls have as many as 60 cows in their groups. Pregnant females give birth to one calf in May or June.

Natural enemies of the American elk include bears, coyotes, and wolves. Elk once roamed over most of North America. Extensive hunting has now limited their range mostly to areas west of the Rocky Mountains.

The European elk *(Alces alces)* is the same species as the American moose. It is the largest European deer, measuring 2.3 m [7.6 ft] at the shoulder and weighing 820 kg [1804 lb]. The bull's antlers may have a spread of

The head of this elephant shrew, with its large eyes and slender snout, is unlike that of the true shrew.

1.8 m [6 ft]. The cow is smaller than the bull and does not have antlers. Both have coarse brown hair and white legs. The European elk is now limited to eastern Europe.

A.J.C./J.J.M.

ELM (elm) The elm is any of 18 species of large, deciduous shade trees that grow throughout North America, Europe, and Asia. The American elm *(Ulmus americana)* reaches heights of 30 m [100 ft] or more, and may live for more than 200 years. Clusters of small, greenish, bell-shaped flowers grow in the axils before the leaves appear. The flowers produce flattened fruits with wings. (*See* DISPERSION OF PLANTS.) These fruits are released as the lopsided, tooth-edged leaves begin to open. Since elm wood is very hard, it is a valuable source of lumber for use in making furniture, barrels, and boats. Elm wood is also a popular fuel.

There are several other important species of elms. Slippery elm *(Ulmus rubra)* has a gluey inner bark which, if chewed, gives relief to a sore throat. It was once used as a treatment for cholera. Rock or cork elm *(Ulmus thomasii)* is known for its corky bark and its extremely hard wood. The English elm *(Ulmus procera)* is the tallest of the elms.

Elm trees are often the victims of disease. Dutch elm disease causes the most widespread destruction of elms. It is caused by a fungus carried by a bark beetle, and results in the death of the tree within a few weeks. Another disease, phloem necrosis, results in the death of the leaves and is caused by a virus carried by the leafhopper insect. Both of these diseases spread very rapidly, often affecting hundreds of trees before their presence is even known. Insecticides and fungicides have had limited success in controlling these diseases. There has been some success, however, in breeding an elm tree which is resistant or immune to these diseases. *See also* CLONE; HYBRID.

A.J.C./M.H.S.

EMBRYO

An embryo (em′ brē ō′) is a living thing in its earliest stages of development. An embryo is formed by the union of a male sex cell with a female sex cell. The sex cells are also called germ cells or gametes. Since these sex cells contain chromosomes from the parents, the embryo inherits characteristics from both parents. (*See* HEREDITY.) In plants, an embryo is the part of the seed that will grow into an adult. The plant embryo is formed by pollination, or the joining of a pollen nucleus (male sex cell) with an egg (female sex cell). In animals, an embryo is produced by fertilization, or the joining of a sperm (male sex cell) with an egg (female sex cell). In both plants and animals, the sex cells have half the number of chromosomes of the adult. When two sex cells join, their chromosomes add up to the number found in the adult. That is, a male sex cell with chromosome number N combines with a female sex cell with chromosome number N to produce an embryo with chromosome number 2N, the same number as in an adult. N is used for chromosome number because different species have different numbers of chromosomes. The chromosome number in the sex cells is half that of other cells because of a process of cellular division called meiosis.

In human beings, an embryo is formed by the joining of a sperm and an egg. During prenatal (before birth) development, a single fertilized egg cell divides and specializes into the billions of cells in the new-born baby. Once the basic body shape and organs have begun to form, usually within eight weeks, the embryo is called a fetus. At the end of a normal, nine month pregnancy, the fetus will be about 50 cm [20 in] long and weigh about 3.3 kg [7.3 lb].

Fertilization of the egg takes place in the

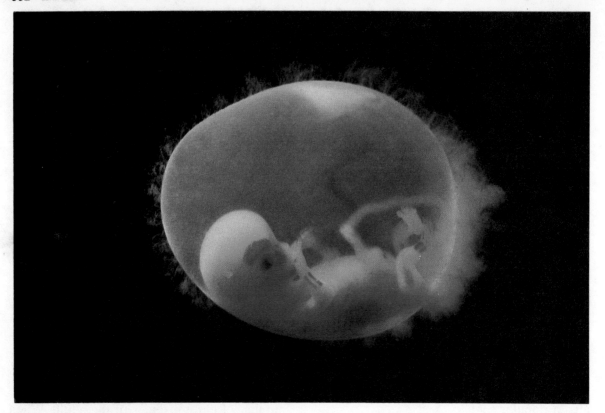

Above, a human embryo at the end of its ninth week of life, about a quarter of the way through its development. It is about 1 inch long.

woman's body in a structure called the fallopian tube. The fallopian tube is part of the female reproductive system and leads from the ovary (where the eggs are produced) to the uterus (where the baby develops). The fertilized egg is called a zygote. As the zygote moves down the fallopian tube toward the uterus, it begins to divide by mitosis. The single fertilized egg cell becomes two cells, then four cells, then eight, and so on until a small solid ball of cells called a morula is formed. This mass of cells continues dividing, forming a hollow, tennis ball-like blastula. The blastula has an inner and an outer layer of cells. In preparation for the blastula, the wall of the uterus becomes thick and rich in blood. (*See* MENSTRUAL CYCLE.) The outer layer of the blastula, the trophoblast, attaches itself to the thickened wall of the uterus, and begins the formation of a placenta and an umbilical cord. These allow oxygen and food to pass from the mother's blood to the baby's blood, and wastes to pass from the baby's blood to the mother's. It takes about two months for the placenta and umbilical cord to be fully developed.

The inner layer of the blastula, the embryoblast, develops into an embryonic disk. The embryonic disk develops into a tube-shaped gastrula with three layers of cells, the outer ectoderm, the inner endoderm, and the middle mesoderm. Each of these layers produces specific structures in the adult. The ectoderm develops into the skin, hair, nails, brain, nervous sytem, part of the eye, and part of the ear. The endoderm produces most of the alimentary canal and its associated organs. It also produces the tissue which lines or surrounds internal organs. The mesoderm develops into most of the internal tissues and organs, such as the heart, kidneys, muscles, bones, and blood.

The development of all of these structures is the result of cellular differentiation. The

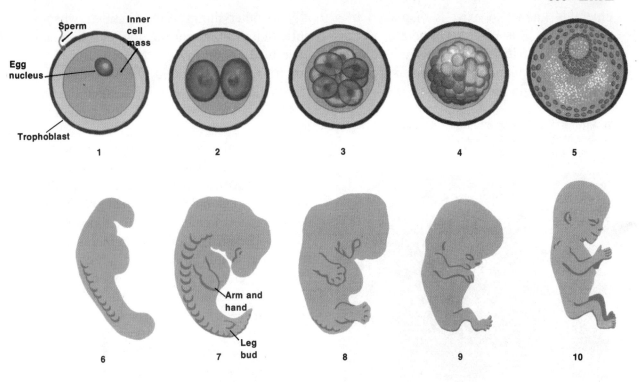

Some stages in the development of the human embryo. 1. A sperm fertilizes the egg. 2. The nucleus of the fertilized egg divides in two. 3. Each cell has divided twice to produce eight. 4. Further divisions produce a blackberrylike mass. 5. The cell mass divides into an outer sphere and an inner cell mass from which the embryo grows. 6. The embryo at 3 1/2 weeks shows the beginnings of the backbone. 7. At 6 weeks the arms have appeared, as well as budlike legs. 8. At 7 weeks growth of the brain increases. 9. At 8 weeks the limbs are recognizably formed. 10. At 12 weeks the embryo is a recognizable baby.

process involved is not clearly understood, but cells specialize to perform certain functions in specific tissues or organs. After about four weeks, the embryo is about 6 mm [0.25 in] long. The head is large and bent over. There are small swellings called buds on the side of the embryo. These buds will develop into arms and legs. There are blocks of tissue called somites arranged along the embryo's body. These somites develop into bones and muscles. Within eight weeks after fertilization, cellular differentiation is virtually complete and the embryo is about 25 mm [1 in] long. These first eight weeks are the most important in the development of the child because it is during this time that all the adult structures are established and begin to grow. At eight weeks, the fetus can be recognized as being human, with human features and structures.

Birth defects, though relatively rare, are usually a result of some malfunction during these first two months. The malfunction may be caused by faulty chromosomes from one or both parents, or by external reasons such as radiation, certain drugs, or certain diseases. (*See* MUTATION.) *See also* GESTATION PERIOD; REPRODUCTION.   A.J.C./E.R.L.

EMERALD (em′ rəld) Emerald, a rich green gemstone, is a variety of the mineral beryl. The highest quality emeralds come from Columbia. Columbia is also the largest producer of these gems. Emeralds are also mined in India, Rhodesia, Russia, and North Carolina.

A natural emerald crystal has a six-sided form. Large and perfect emeralds are about equal in value to diamonds. One of the largest emeralds known to exist is displayed in a museum in Russia. This emerald weighs about 2.7 kg [6 lbs]. The oriental emerald is a form of the mineral corundum, not beryl as the name would indicate.   J.J.A./R.H.

A natural emerald crystal has a six-sided form. All emeralds except Oriental emeralds are forms of the mineral beryl.

EMERY (em′ rē) Emery, a dull gray material, is a variety of the mineral corundum. Emery is mined chiefly in Russia and the United States.

Emery is used to grind metals, gems, and optical lenses. Emery is first crushed into tiny pieces or a fine powder. It may then be mounted on paper or mixed with cement and formed into grinding wheels. Manufactured abrasives, such as aluminum oxide and silicon carbide, have largely replaced emery.
                    J.J.A./R.H.

EMOTION (i mō′ shən) Emotion is a reaction involving a strong feeling or feelings. Common emotions include joy, love, hope, desire, fear, anger, hate, and sadness. Emotional reactions can be aroused by thoughts or outside events.

A child is born with emotional reactions to only a few things, such as pain and hunger. However, he soon learns to respond emotionally to other things. For example, when a child first meets a snarling dog, the child may have no emotion toward the dog. But if the dog tries to bite the child, the child develops fear toward the dog. Having learned the fear of snarling dogs, the child avoids them in the future.

Emotional responses are an important form of self-defense. They result in bodily changes that help to give protection against danger. For example, the adrenal glands pour the hormone adrenaline into the bloodstream when a person is afraid. This increases the rate of the heartbeat and the depth of breathing, and releases emergency food supplies for use by the muscles. All these help the person to meet the danger or flee from it.

Emotional responses may also be harmful. If the body changes caused by emotions continue for a long time, vital tissue damage can result. For example, constant fear can produce stomach ulcers. Strong emotions can make it hard to think and to solve problems. A student taking a test may be so worried about failing that he or she cannot think properly. The worry drains mental energy needed for the test. *See also* PSYCHOSOMATIC DISORDER.
                    J.J.A./J.J.F.

EMULSION (i məl′ shən) Emulsion is a preparation of one liquid dispersed, or evenly distributed, in another. The two liquids do not dissolve in each other. Tiny drops of the dispersed liquid remain suspended in the other liquid. (*See* COLLOID.)

Emulsions are not stable. The liquids usually separate from each other after a certain time. An emulsifying agent, such as soap, may be needed to stabilize the emulsion and prevent it from separating.

Common substances such as cosmetic lotions, foods, lubricants, medicines, and paints are emulsions.

Oil and water form the most common emulsions. An emulsion can be formed by either droplets of oil dispersed in water or droplets of water in oil. For example, milk is an emulsion of butterfat in water. The emulsifying agent that keeps butterfat suspended in milk is the protein casein. *See also* SUSPENSION.   J.J.A./A.D.

ENAMEL (in am' əl) Enamel is a glasslike substance applied as a coating to metal and ceramic objects. It is produced in many colors. Enamel is commonly used as a protective surface for such things as cooking utensils, and kitchen and bathroom fixtures.

An enamel coating is applied to an object by first grinding sand, borax, and metallic compounds into a fine mixture of particles. This mixture is applied to the object to be enameled by melting (firing) the mixture onto the metal. The heat melts the enamel and combines it with the surface of the article.

There are several types of decorative enameling. Cloisonné or celled enamel is made by bending and soldering metal strips together to make a design. The holes in the design are filled with different colored mixtures and the object is fired. The heat melts the enamel to bind it with the metal. Champlevé or inlaid enamel is made by filling designs engraved in metal with enamel.

J.M.C./A.D.

ENDOCRINE (en' də krən) The term "endocrine" refers to a type of gland. An endocrine gland is a group of cells that have special functions in regulating the body.

Glands make chemical substances. Those glands that send out their secretions directly to the body tissues through ducts are called exocrine. Examples of the exocrine glands include the salivary glands, which produce saliva in the mouth; lachrymal, or tear glands; and sweat glands.

The endocrine glands secrete their hormones directly into the blood stream, without passing through a duct. They are located in various parts of the body. Each gland has one or more specific jobs to do. For example, the

pituitary gland is located at the base of the brain. It is called the "master" endocrine gland because it controls the action of some of the other glands. Other endocrine glands include the thyroid gland, the adrenal glands, the pineal, and the pancreas.

The endocrine glands are very important. If one of them is not working the way it should, serious disease or death can result. The endocrine gland system is very complicated. It has been studied extensively by medical specialists, called endocrinologists.

P.G.C./J.J.F.

ENDOSPERM (en' də spərm') An endosperm is a food-storing tissue that surrounds and nourishes the embryo in a seed. In some seeds, such as the bean and the pea, the endosperm is completely absorbed before the seed matures. In others, such as wheat, part of the endosperm remains until the seed germinates. (*See* GERMINATION.) It is the endosperm that provides most of the edible material in cereal crops and in oil-producing seeds, such as corn. The coconut has a liquid endosperm, the coconut milk.

In angiosperms, the endosperm contains three sets of chromosomes instead of the usual two. This condition (3N) results from the fusion, or joining, of one pollen nucleus (N) with two polar bodies (N, N) in the ovary of the pistil. Polar bodies are produced as "side products" when an egg divides by meiosis. *See also* CHROMOSOME; GAMETE.

A.J.C./M.H.S.

ENDOSPORE (en' də spōr') An endospore is a thick-walled cell which is well-suited for dormancy and can tolerate many unfavorable environmental conditions. Endospores are an important part of asexual reproduction in certain algae and fungi.

Some bacteria, usually the rod-shaped bacilli, produce endospores which may be dormant for years. These endospores can withstand extreme conditions, such as boiling or freezing, without damage. When conditions become favorable, the endospores develop into bacteria. Endospores are a major cause of food poisoning in improperly processed foods. Fortunately, few pathogenic (disease-causing) bacteria produce endospores. *See also* BOTULISM; FOOD PRESERVATION.

A.J.C./M.H.S.

ENDOTHERMIC REACTION (en' də thər' mik rē ak' shən) An endothermic reaction is a chemical reaction that absorbs heat. Endothermic reactions are important in the cooling of food. For example, if several ice cubes are placed in a warm drink, the ice absorbs heat as it melts. Eventually, if there is enough ice, the temperature of the drink drops to the temperature of the ice cubes, 0°C [32°F].

A chemical reaction that gives off heat is called an exothermic reaction.   J.M.C./A.D.

ENERGY

If anything can do work, then it is said to possess energy (en' ər jē). To carry out any task, we need to perform work. Machines are capable of doing work. Work is required to dig a garden or to saw a block of wood, for example.

There are many different kinds of energy. All living things need energy to grow. Plants get energy from the light of the sun. This is electromagnetic energy. (*See* PHOTOSYNTHESIS.) Plants also feed through their roots and get energy from the nutrients thus acquired. Heat and light are both forms of energy. Animals get their energy by eating plants and other animals. The food is digested and provides a source of chemical energy for the animal. We need energy to heat our

Different forms of energy. 1. Water stored in a dam illustrates potential energy. 2. Motion is a form of kinetic energy. 3. An atomic reactor harnesses nuclear energy. 4. The panels on this satellite collect solar energy. 5. Power lines carry electrical energy from one place to another. 6. A burning fire is an example of chemical energy.

1

2

3

4

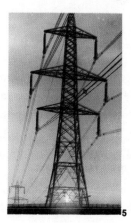
5

6

houses. This energy is often provided by burning fuels, such as coal or gas. Fuels contain chemical energy. When they are burned, the chemical energy is turned into heat energy. This is one example of energy conversion. Most forms of energy can be converted into other forms. Energy conversion is often used to convert one form of energy into another, more useful, form.

If an object is moving, the energy of its movement is called kinetic energy. When you run, the fact that you are moving means that you possess kinetic energy. This energy comes from the chemical energy of the food that you eat. Another kind of energy is called potential energy. This is stored energy. When you wind up a clock you are converting the kinetic energy of the turning key into potential energy. This potential energy is stored either in the tightly wound spring or in the weights of a pendulum clock. When you wind up a pendulum clock you raise the weights. As the weights slowly fall under gravity their potential energy is converted back into the kinetic energy of the moving gears, levers, and hands.

The water behind a dam also has potential energy. If the dam were to break, the water would rush down the valley. The potential energy would have been converted into the kinetic energy of the moving water. The potential energy of the water can be used to produce electricity. The water flows through a turbine and causes its blades to rotate. The potential energy of the water behind the dam is converted to the kinetic energy of moving water, which is then turned into the kinetic energy of the blades. A generator then converts the kinetic energy into electrical energy. (*See* GENERATOR; HYDROELECTRIC POWER.)

Albert Einstein was one of the greatest physicists of all time. (*See* EINSTEIN, ALBERT.) He was the first person to show that mass is equivalent to energy. A mass of one kilogram converts to the amount of energy a large power station produces in three years.

One might think that the mass of a nucleus would be the same as the mass of its protons and neutrons. In fact, the mass of the nucleus is a little smaller. When protons and neutrons form a nucleus, some of their mass disappears. It is converted into nuclear energy to bind these particles together.

A nuclear power station converts some of this nuclear energy into electrical energy. Nuclear energy can also be used destructively, as in a nuclear weapon. Stars contain huge amounts of energy. We see some of this energy as light. This energy comes from nuclear energy. Stars "burn" their mass into energy.

Conservation of energy One form of energy can change into another. But if the mass of the system does not change, the total amount of energy always remains the same. This is the law of the conservation of energy. For example, when 3.8 liters [1 gallon] of gasoline is burned in a car engine, about 100,000 kilojoules of chemical energy are converted into heat energy. Although only about 25,000 kJ (kilojoules) are actually used in driving the car, the remaining 75,000 kJ do not disappear. They are wasted by heating up the engine's cooling water and heating up the air with the exhaust gases. Some energy, too, is used in overcoming the friction forces in the engine. But you could do a sum to show that the heat energy produced by the fuel is equal to the energy used in driving the car added to the energy wasted in heating up the surroundings.

If nuclear energy is involved in the energy change, the change in the mass of the fuel has to be taken into account. Then the law of the conservation of energy becomes the law of the conservation of mass and energy. In this case the energy produced during a day is equal to the loss in the mass of the fuel during the day.

Energy supplies The economic law of supply and demand applies to energy as well as to

The solar photograph (facing left) shows an eruption on the sun's surface.

goods and services. The price we pay for something is influenced by what happens to the supply or demand for it. When oil is in short supply, the price of its by-products—gasoline, for example—will rise. So would the price of the oil and gas we use to heat our homes and factories. Oil and gas are natural sources of energy. They come from fossil fuels that were stored in the earth millions of years ago. This supply is limited and is running out.

Once again, coal is claiming the attention of business and industry. This fossil fuel exists in great abundance. But it fell into disfavor when oil and natural gas became more available. Electricity also helped to displace coal as an energy source. All of these newer energy sources are clean. They do not pollute the air as burning coal does. If this drawback of coal could be solved, our energy supply would be assured for many years. The application of total automation to mining and processing could get coal out of the ground in sufficient quantity to meet the energy demands of our growing population. But this will take time.

Meanwhile, other sources of energy might help solve the problem of supply. Nuclear energy is a possible solution. But nuclear processes produce large quantities of dangerous wastes. And many people are afraid to live near, or work in, nuclear-powered industries that might accidentally emit radiation. A safer source would be the geothermal energy that lies deep in the earth. This heat energy comes to the surface as geysers and volcanic

The wind turbine (right) can, in a 13 kilometer-per-hour [8 mph] wind, produce enough energy to be used by fifty average homes.

eruptions. Some geothermal sources are hot enough to be of practical use in turning turbines that generate electricity. Geothermal power already is serving the needs of more than a million people in one part of California. But a disadvantage of tapping geothermal energy sources is its possible destructive effect on the environment.

Another likely source is thermonuclear reactions. Such reactions occur in the sun and other stars. With increased understanding of them, scientists hope to find an application on earth. This method would supply us with huge amounts of energy. But many technical problems are involved. However, much progress has been made in utilizing the radiant energy of the sun directly. Solar heating of homes and other buildings is gaining acceptance. And solar cells and solar batteries for converting radiant energy to electricity are finding other than space flight uses.

Still another possibility lies in the kinetic energy of tides. Some countries are already using this energy source but only on a small scale. In America, the windmill is making a comeback—mostly as a turbine for generating electricity.

M.E./J.T.

ENGINE

An engine (en′ jən) is a device that uses the energy in a fuel to do work. The energy in the chemicals of the fuel is first turned into heat energy. The heat is then used to move the metal parts of a machine. There are many kinds of fuel. Most engines use gasoline, oil, kerosene, coal, or coke. The heat that comes from burning the fuel makes a gas expand. This expanded gas drives pistons or turbine blades. The pistons or turbines turn shafts. The turning shafts move gears and other wheels. We use these rotating wheels and shafts to move automobiles, airplanes, and other transport. We can also use them for

pumping, drilling, digging, and other such activities.

Early engines burned coal or wood to heat water. The steam was used to drive steam engines. Until the middle of this century, most locomotives were powered by steam. At the beginning of the century, even some automobiles were run on steam. We still use steam engines, but most of them are being replaced by more efficient engines. Today we have powerful gasoline and diesel engines to work for us.

The gasoline engine   The engines of most automobiles and small vehicles use gasoline as fuel. The gasoline engine is an internal-combustion engine. The fuel is burned in combustion (burning) chambers inside the engine. The combustion chambers are placed at one end of the cylinders. Pistons move up and down in the cylinders. They are pushed by the hot gases from the burning fuel. When the fuel is mixed with air it burns so quickly that it explodes. The combustion chambers and cylinders are made strong enough not to break during the explosion. Instead of blowing the cylinder apart like a bomb, the explosion simply kicks hard against the head of the piston. It pushes it as far as it can.

Each movement of a piston up or down in its cylinder is called a stroke. Most gasoline engines work on a four-stroke cycle. This means that each piston goes up and down twice for each explosion. That makes four movements or strokes. This cycle of events is repeated over and over again. On the first downstroke, the piston moves to the lowest part of the cylinder. A mixture of gasoline droplets and air is drawn into the cylinder above it. Now the piston moves up again. This is its second stroke. It squeezes the mixture into a small space. An electric spark lights the mixture, and it explodes. The piston is forced down again for its third stroke. This is called the power stroke. For the fourth stroke, the piston moves to the top again. This time it pushes the burnt gases out of the cylinder. The gases leave the engine as exhaust fumes.

The first engine that used the four-stroke cycle was made in about 1876. It was designed by the German engineer, Nikolaus August Otto. He used coal gas, not gasoline. The first engines to burn gasoline were developed by Karl Benz and Gottlieb Daimler. These two men were famous as automobile pioneers. (*See* AUTOMOBILE.)

A piston simply going up and down cannot push an automobile along. Its movement must be changed to a turning movement. To do this, a crankshaft is used. Each piston of the engine is linked to part of the crankshaft. Each push it gives makes the shaft turn. The spinning shaft passes the power on to the automobile's transmission system. It usually does this through a heavy flywheel. The transmission system transmits power to the clutch and to the propeller shaft, through a gearbox. The propeller shaft drives the road wheels by means of axles.

To keep an automobile engine going, there need to be several systems. There must be a fuel system. This has to supply gasoline to the engine cylinders in the right amounts. It has also to mix it with the right amount of air, so that it will explode properly. There must be an ignition system. This has to provide sparks to ignite the explosive mixture at exactly the right time. There has to be a cooling system, otherwise the engine would overheat. The lubrication system must keep all the moving parts oiled and moving freely. Too much friction causes wear of the metal and makes the engine overheat.

The engine unit The gasoline engine has two basic parts. They are called the cylinder head and the cylinder block. The cylinder block is machined from solid metal. The metal is usually cast iron. Sometimes aluminum is used because it is much lighter. It also carries heat away quickly. Inside the cylinder block are the cylinders. The walls of the cylinders have to be very accurately made, and are highly polished. The pistons that move up and down in the cylinders must be accurately made, too. They have springy bands of metal around them to press tight against the cylinder walls and stop gases leaking. The bands are called piston rings. They are often made of aluminum alloy for strength and lightness.

An engine may have any number of cylinders. They may be arranged in a line, or in opposite pairs. If they are in pairs, they are often arranged in a "V" shape. In many airplanes with piston engines, the cylinders are arranged in a ring around the crankshaft.

The lower part of the cylinder block is called the crankcase. This is where the crankshaft lies. The crankshaft is linked to each piston by a connecting rod. The crankshaft is made in a single piece. It must be tough and accurately machined. It may spin as many as 6,000 times a minute. It changes the up-and-down motion of the piston into a turning motion. It does this by means of cranks, one for each piston. The cranks are set at different angles round the shaft. Each piston gives a push to its crank during its power stroke. During the other three strokes, the crank pushes the piston up, down and up again. The heavy flywheel is bolted to one end of the crankshaft. It keeps the shaft turning smoothly between the power strokes. Strong main bearings support the crankshaft in its case.

The cylinder head is bolted to the cylinder block. Inside it are the combustion chambers. Each combustion chamber is a space above a piston inside a cylinder. This is where the explosion of the mixture of fuel and air takes place. A spark plug is set into the top of the chamber. Each chamber has a pair of valves. There is an inlet valve to allow the fuel and air mixture into the chamber. The other valve is an outlet or exhaust valve. Through this pass the burnt gases after the explosion. The valves are opened and closed by push rods and springs. The push rods are moved up and down by links with the crankshaft. The linkage is through a turning shaft called the camshaft.

To carry water to cool the engine, there are passages in the metal of the cylinder head and cylinder block. Oil passes through other passages. Between the cylinder head and block is a gasket. This is a thin plate of metal that acts as a seal. It is put in when the parts of the engine are bolted together. It is often made of copper.

The fuel system The fuel system of the engine supplies the gasoline to be burnt. The gasoline is stored in a large tank. In a powerful car, the tank holds many gallons of fuel. The tank is placed well away from the engine, to reduce the risk of fire. The gasoline is pumped through a fuel line. The pump may be driven by links with the engine camshaft. Sometimes it has its own electric motor. Before the gasoline reaches the cylinders, it must be mixed with air. The fuel line leads to the carburetor. In the carburetor the gasoline is forced through a fine nozzle, or jet. It forms a spray of small droplets. The droplets vaporize as they mix with the air. Now the mixture is ready for ignition.

The speed of the engine is controlled by a throttle valve. Opening and closing the throttle valve regulates the amount of mixture leaving the carburetor. From the carburetor the mixture passes to the inlet valves of the combustion chambers. The mixture is delivered through a set of tubes called the inlet manifold. A similar set of tubes takes away exhaust gases from the exhaust valves of the combustion chambers. This is called the exhaust manifold. It leads to the outside air through the exhaust pipe. The exhaust pipe is fitted with a muffler, or silencer, to reduce noise.

In some automobiles, the fuel is delivered by a different system. Instead of passing through a carburetor, the fuel is sprayed into the airstream just before the inlet valves. It is sprayed in small amounts, which are carefully metered. The system is called fuel injection.

The ignition system The mixture inside each cylinder must be made to explode. A spark is used to do this. The spark must jump across the gap in the spark plug at exactly the right time. Each of the automobile's cylinders must fire in turn. The ignition system depends upon very accurate timing. If the sparks are a fraction of a second too early or too late, the engine will not run properly.

The electricity to make the sparks comes from the automobile's electric storage battery. This battery is kept charged by a dynamo, or generator, run by the engine. The battery supplies electricity at only about 12 volts. To make a spark, thousands of volts are required. The voltage from the battery is boosted up to about 30,000 volts by means of a transformer. The transformer is called the ignition coil. The ignition coil supplies high voltage to the distributor. This is a device that "distributes" electricity in surges, or pulses, to each of the spark plugs in turn. When a surge of electricity at high voltage reaches a plug, a spark leaps across a small gap. The spark is so hot that it makes the mixture of gasoline and air ignite and explode.

The cooling system The heat produced by burning the gasoline in the engine is very great. The temperature inside each combustion chamber may reach more than 1,000°C [over 1,800°F]. The engine must be constantly cooled. The cooling system supplies cool water through channels called water jackets. The water jackets surround the cylinders. They carry away the excess heat as the water passes through them. The hot water is led away to be cooled in the radiator. The radiator is a system of many tubes, linked together, with spaces between them. Cold air from the front of the autuombile rushes between the tubes. A fan, driven by the engine,

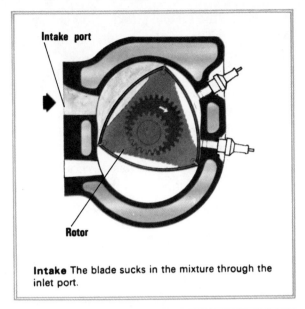

Intake The blade sucks in the mixture through the inlet port.

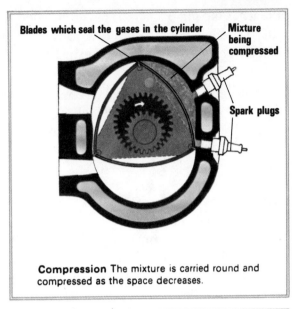

Compression The mixture is carried round and compressed as the space decreases.

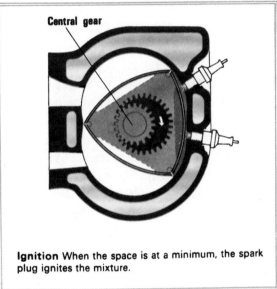

Ignition When the space is at a minimum, the spark plug ignites the mixture.

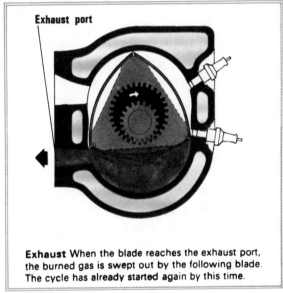

Exhaust When the blade reaches the exhaust port, the burned gas is swept out by the following blade. The cycle has already started again by this time.

The illustrations above show the sequence of events in the workings of a Wankel engine.

speeds up the flow of air. The hot water loses its heat to the air. The cooled water is then pumped to the engine again.

Some automobiles do not have a water-cooled system. They use air cooling. Air from the front of the automobile is blown over the cylinder block and the cylinder head. The engine is fitted with special cooling fins, sticking out into the airstream. These help the heat to radiate more quickly. Air-cooled engines tend to be noisier than water-cooled engines.

In a water-cooled engine, the water jacket helps to absorb the engine noise.

To prevent the water in the cooling system from freezing in cold weather, antifreeze is usually added in winter. This is often ethylene glycol or a similar compound.

The lubrication system Oil is needed to keep the engine's parts from wearing too quickly. A storage tank of oil, called the sump, is attached under the crankcase. The oil is pumped through channels to all the main bearings and the big-end bearings. Eventually it reaches the sump again. It passes through a filter to remove dirt before it is used again. Whenever metal surfaces rub against others, tiny particles are worn off. The oil picks them up as it flows between the surfaces. They are trapped by the oil filter. The filter must be changed regularly. The oil itself gradually burns and becomes impure. It must be replaced at intervals.

The Wankel engine   The Wankel engine is a gasoline engine that works without pistons. It was invented in Germany by Felix Wankel. He started development of it in 1956. The pistons in an ordinary gasoline engine must move up and down, or backwards and forwards. This kind of motion is called reciprocating motion. It needs to be converted into a turning motion (rotary motion) by a crankshaft. In a Wankel engine, burning the fuel produces a rotary motion directly. There is no need for a crankshaft. It is a rotary engine.

A Wankel engine has a specially designed combustion chamber. It is roughly an ellipse, or oval, in shape. Inside is a rotor. The rotor is shaped like a triangle with bulging, rounded sides. Through the center of the rotor passes the driving shaft. It has teeth like a gearwheel that meet teeth inside the rotor. The rotor is shaped so that its corners just touch the walls of the chamber. The rotor can move up and down and also side to side as it turns.

The rotor divides the chamber into three parts. As the rotor turns, the shapes of the three parts change. They act like three separate combustion chambers. As in an ordinary engine, there are spark plugs, an inlet port for the gasoline and air mixture, and an outlet port for the exhaust gases.

The rotor turns so that each part of the chamber in turn meets the inlet. The gasoline and air mixture is drawn in. This is like the first piston downstroke of an ordinary engine. Further turning sweeps the mixture round into a smaller space. The mixture is compressed.

This is like the second stroke. Now the spark plug fires. The explosion drives the rotor further around. This is the power stroke. When the rotor has turned a little further, the exhaust gases are pushed from the chamber through the exhaust port. The process is continuous. It happens as each part of the chamber sweeps round.

The Wankel engine has several advantages over an ordinary engine. It has fewer moving parts. There is less vibration. It is lighter. It costs less to produce. However, there are difficulties. The main difficulty is ensuring that the seals, where the corners of the rotor meet the chamber walls, are gastight. The Wankel engine is used successfully in several kinds of automobile. *See also:* DIESEL; JET PROPULSION; SOLAR ENERGY.

D.W./J.T.

ENGINEERING (en′ jə nir′ ing) Engineering deals with the ways in which we use natural materials for our own purposes. It covers a very wide field. It deals with everything from designing a new rocket to building huge skyscrapers. Some engineers specialize in electrical equipment. Others make a special study of plastics. Others are experts in building safe bridges. There are many specializations. But all engineers have one thing in common. They put scientific knowledge to practical use.

A few hundred years ago, there were only two divisions of engineering. Military engineering dealt with weapons and engines for warfare. Military engineers built roads for soldiers to use, and fortified walls and ditches for defense. The Roman armies had expert engineers. Some great scientists, such as Leonardo da Vinci, put their minds to military problems. Civil engineering dealt with the building of roads, bridges, canals, and aqueducts for towns and cities. Early civil engineers designed irrigation systems for the

The three engineers (facing right) are examining the blueprints of a building project.

countryside. This made it possible for agriculture to support city life. Some of the roads, bridges, sewers, and canals built hundreds of years ago are still in use today.

The greatest advances in engineering have been in the last 200 years. During these centuries scientific knowledge has grown very rapidly. Engineers have become specialists in particular fields. Today we can divide engineering into five main branches. These are: civil, mechanical, mining and metallurgical, chemical, and electrical engineering.

Civil engineering   Civil engineering is the design and building of roads, bridges, waterways, airports, canals, dams, sewers, railroads, hospitals, and other public buildings. Safety is most important in all construction of this kind. Engineers must study soils and rocks so that they can decide the correct foundations to build. They must know the strengths of all the materials they use. They must know the maximum load that is safe for bridges. They have to know how much water a dam can safely hold.

Architects and civil engineers work closely together. An architect is responsible for producing a pleasing and efficient design. It is the civil engineer's job to check that suitable materials are used to build a structure. It is no use having a good-looking bridge that is unsafe. Teams of experts work together on big projects.

Civil engineers also have to know about the equipment that is used in building. They have to decide how to move materials, using cranes, bulldozers, mechanical shovels, and other vehicles. They give advice about everything from welding girders to using a pile-driver. Civil engineering is one of the biggest branches of engineering. It covers many specialities.

Mechanical engineering   Mechanical engineers are the experts in machinery. They are concerned with using energy to produce mechanical power. Every industry you can think of uses machines of some kind. The farmer uses tractors, seed-drills and sprayers. In a plastics factory there are hundreds of machines, for melting, mixing, molding, rolling, and stamping. New machinery is in demand all the time. It is the job of mechanical engineers to design and construct machines.

In the power-producing industries, specialized machinery is needed. Different kinds of machinery and equipment are used to produce power from natural resources. Mechanical engineers have to deal with coal, natural gas, oil, and other fuels in power-producing plants. Nuclear fuels require machinery of a different kind.

Aeronautical engineering is a specialized kind of engineering dealing with aircraft. Automotive engineering deals with the design and building of automobiles. Marine engineering deals not only with ships and submarines, but with docks and other equipment. There are numerous other specialities in mechanical engineering.

Mining and metallurgical engineering   This deals with the ways that ores and minerals can be discovered and brought up from the earth. It also deals with the ways that metals can be extracted from their ores and prepared for use. A mining engineer work closely with geologists, who study the rock in the earth.

Mining engineers must know the best way to construct mine shafts in different circumstances. They must know about machinery to ventilate the shafts. They must know about drills and digging equipment to extract minerals from the earth. Mining engineers may specialize in coal mining, uranium mining, gold mining, or another field. They need a sound knowledge of civil, mechanical, and electrical engineering.

Metallurgical engineers are experts in separating minerals from their ores and preparing them for use. Another name for metallurgical engineer is extractive metallurgist. He or she deals with how to get the metal iron from different kinds of iron ore. A physical metallurgist tests minerals and metals for strength and hardness.

Chemical engineering Chemical engineering deals with the ways raw materials can be changed into useful products. A chemical engineer may be a specialist in one chemical process. He or she may specialize in making paint, dyes, fertilizers, plastics, soaps, explosives, drugs, or one of hundreds of other things. The chemical engineer must understand how to handle large quantities of chemicals. Some chemicals are very dangerous. To handle them safely needs an expert knowledge. Some chemicals may need special equipment to transport them. This is the chemical engineer's job.

There are numerous different processes for which chemical engineers may be responsible. Some of them are distillation, crystallization, filtration, mixing, crushing, and drying of chemical compounds.

Electrical engineering Electrical engineering deals with the construction and use of different kinds of electrical equipment. Electrical equipment is used in power plants, radio and television stations, radar, telephones, and air-conditioning systems.

Electricity generators may be run by water power, nuclear power, or coal or oil. There are many specialist electrical engineers. Electronics engineers design and build miniature electronic circuits. Communications engineers are experts in radio, television, radar, and telephones. D.M.H.W./R.W.L.

ENTOMOLOGY (ent′ ə mäl′ ə jē) Entomology is the study of insects. This vast group includes three-fourths of the known animal species. Entomologists (scientists who study insects) study the anatomy, physiology, behavior, ecology, and classi-fication of insects. The field of entomology often also includes organisms closely related to insects, like spiders and centipedes.

Many entomologists study the effects that insects have on human life. For example, medical entomologists study insects that carry diseases, like the mosquitos. Some entomologists study the effect of insects on farm crops, while others study certain insects called parasites that live off other organisms. Scientists often develop insecticides to kill harmful insects if they discover how and why an insect's body works. Harmful insects are now often deliberately controlled by other means, such as by using insects' parasites or diseases or by sterilizing the males so they can not produce offspring.

Entomology helps people to understand the function of insects in the ecosystems of the earth. Today, entomologists realize that most insects are beneficial or harmless to humans and their crops and animals. J.M.C./J.R.

ENTROPY (en′ trə pē) Entropy is a measure of the internal disorder of matter. At a temperature of absolute zero, all the atoms and molecules of a crystal stop moving and are held in fixed positions. At such a time, there is no disorder. The atoms in a diamond crystal, at room temperature, are held by chemical bonds in a rigid framework. The only movement is the vibration of the atoms. But a few of the atoms escape from the framework and there is a small amount of disorder, or entropy. Atoms of helium gas in a balloon are very disordered. They move about within the balloon, colliding with each other and with the walls of the balloon. Helium gas has a higher entropy than a diamond.

Entropy is a very useful idea in some heat calculations. (*See* THERMODYNAMICS.) It is also used in information theory to describe how well a system can handle information. A system that has a high degree of unpredictability has high entropy. *See also* ABSOLUTE ZERO; BOND, CHEMICAL. W.R.P./A.I.

Above, the Eastern Highlands of New Guinea are a natural environment largely undisturbed by the growth of industrial civilization.

ENVIRONMENT (in vī′ rən mənt) Every organism is affected by many outside influences. These influences include: soil, air, water, temperature, chemicals, amount of sunlight, wind, and many other things. These influences are commonly referred to as environmental conditions. The total of all environmental conditions acting upon an organism is its environment.

There are many different environments. The environment of a forest is often well-shaded, cool, and moist. The desert environment is usually hot and dry. The environment at the bottom of the ocean is cold and dark, with a tremendous amount of pressure. The environment of a place will determine what organisms can live at that place. An oak tree will not grow at the bottom of an ocean, nor will a fish live on desert sands. Often, organisms are able to change an environment. (*See* SUCCESSION.)

Humans are able to change environments more than any other organism. They can move mountains, dam rivers, drain lakes, and even make it rain. By changing the environment around them, humans have been able to make life more comfortable. They may now live anywhere they choose. (*See* ADAPTATION.) People can also do great harm to the earth by changing environments. They have caused floods, droughts, the extinction of animals, the spread of diseases, and the spoiling of air and water. (*See* POLLUTION.) We now realize that we must not make great changes in our environment because it is impossible to do just one thing to the environment. If we do one thing, many other unplanned things may also result. *See also* CONSERVATION; ECOLOGY; ECOSYSTEM; POLLUTION.

S.R.G./R.J.B.

ENZYME (en′ zīm′) Enzymes are proteins made in the cells of plants and animals. They cause or speed up chemical reactions. The millions of chemical reactions that make up the metabolism of an organism are controlled by enzymes.

Unlike most chemical reactions, an enzyme-controlled reaction occurs at about the body temperature of an organism—about 37°C [98.6°F] in humans. A chemical reaction that requires high temperature to occur outside the body, like the breakdown of sugar, occurs at the body temperature when it is enzyme-controlled. The body breaks down sugar in a rapid series of enzyme-controlled reactions that release energy slowly. In this way, the body benefits as much as possible from each chemical reaction.

Enzymes are very sensitive substances and may become inactive at high temperature. If a person's body temperature rises to 42°C [108°F], many enzymes stop working, and death becomes a possibility.

An enzyme works by attaching itself to another chemical substance called a substrate. The substrate-enzyme complex goes through the chemical reaction, after which it is released unchanged. Some enzymes need an additional substance to allow attachment to the substrate. These substances are called co-enzymes. Many vitamins are co-enzymes.

Some methods of chemical and biological warfare use poisons that combine with enzymes so as to inactivate them. If enough enzymes are blocked, death may occur. *See also* BIOCHEMISTRY.

J.M.C./J.M.

EOCENE EPOCH (ē′ ə sēn′ ep′ ək) The Eocene epoch is the part of the Tertiary period which started about 55 million years ago and lasted about 15 million years. Mammals were well established by this time. Small ancestors of the horse and camel appeared. Primitive whales and rodents developed during this epoch.

Many modern plants lived during the Eocene epoch, including fruits, flowering plants, and grasses. *See also* GEOLOGICAL TIME SCALE. J.M.C./W.R.S.

EPHEMERAL PLANT (i fem′ rəl plant) An ephemeral plant is one which lives for only a short time. Weeds and some other plants produce seeds which germinate, grow, flower, produce new seeds, and die, all within a few weeks. Most ephemeral plants produce one or more generations each year. The seeds of some ephemeral plants are coated with a chemical inhibitor which prevents growth. This chemical must be washed off by heavy rainfall before the seed will germinate. In this way, the seed remains dormant until there is enough water to support growth. (*See* DORMANCY.) A.J.C./M.H.S.

EPIDEMIC (ep′ ə dem′ ik) An epidemic is the widespread outbreak of a disease. If it is a serious disease, an epidemic may kill thousands of people. In the fourteenth century, the Black Death, an epidemic of bubonic plague, swept across Europe and killed one quarter of the population. A worldwide epidemic is called a pandemic. J.M.C./J.J.F.

EPILEPSY (ep′ ə lep′ sē) Epilepsy is a disturbance of the activity of certain cells in the brain. People with epilepsy have attacks or seizures. The seizure occurs when the nerve cells controlling muscular activity do not operate properly. There are three types of seizures: grand mal, petit mal, and psychomotor.

The grand mal attack is the most severe. It

Epidemics of bubonic plague ("the black death") swept Europe repeatedly between the 14th and 17th centuries. Strange costumes like the above were worn to guard against infection.

is a form of convulsion, sometimes called a "fit." The person loses consciousness and may fall if he or she is not supported. The muscles jerk violently. The seizure lasts a few minutes, then the person may go into a deep sleep.

The petit mal attack is a milder form of seizure. The person may lose awareness, or "go blank." The seizure lasts for only a few seconds, and the person may not even realize he or she has had an attack. Most petit mal attacks occur in children.

During a psychomotor seizure, the person acts strangely for only a few minutes. Sometimes the person walks around aimlessly or tugs at his or her clothes.

Epileptic seizures may occur at any time. Some persons have frequent attacks; others have only a few. They seem to have no direct relationship to the emotional condition of the person.

Very little is known about the causes of epilepsy. It could be caused by brain damage due to infection, by physical injury, or by a tumor. Epilepsy, however, is not contagious.

Doctors treat epilepsy with certain drugs which reduce the seizures or eliminate them. With proper treatment, most epileptics can lead normal lives. P.G.C./J.J.F.

EPIPHYTE (ep′ ə fīt′) An epiphyte is any plant that grows upon another plant for physical support. It is distinguished from a climbing plant which has roots in the ground, and from a parasitic plant which gets its food from its host. Epiphytes are often called air plants. They have specially modified roots and leaves which absorb water and minerals from moisture in the air. They have no attachment to the ground of other source of nutrients. Most epiphytes are tropical. These include orchids, ferns, and members of the cactus family. Some temperate varieties include mosses, liverworts, lichens, and algae. A.J.C./M.H.S.

EPITHELIUM (ep′ ə thē′ lē əm) Epithelium is an important living tissue found in human beings, some animals, and a few plants. It is made up of cells that are closely bound to each other to form sheets. Epithelial tissue has one or more of the following functions: protection, absorption, or secretion.

In human beings, epithelium covers the body and lines the passages of systems that open to the outside. In other words, epithelium lines the alimentary canal as well as the respiratory, reproductive, and excretory tracts.

There are three main types of epithelium, based on cell structure. Squamous epithelium is made of thin, flattened cells with irregular edges. It lines the mouth and esophagus, and is part of the skin. Cuboidal epithelium is made of small, boxlike cells. It lines some body cavities and helps make up some of the glands. Columnar epithelium has long, nar-

row, column-shaped cells. It lines most of the alimentary canal and makes up part of the skin. Some specialized columnar epithelial cells have hairlike structures called cilia. Cilia function to move fluids or other substances in one direction. Ciliated epithelium lines much of the respiratory system (bronchi, trachea, nasal passages), female reproductive system (fallopian tubes, uterus), and male reproductive system (vas deferens, epididymis). A.J.C./E.R.L.

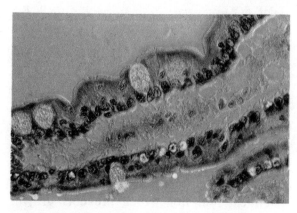

Epithelium is the cell tissue which forms the outer layer of the skin and the lining of most body cavities. Above, a greatly magnified cross-section of a villus, one of the thousands of tiny projections in the epithelium of the small intestine.

EPSOM SALT (ep′ səm sȯlt′) Epsom salt is a powdered form of magnesium sulfate. It is named for the springs in Epsom, England, where it was first obtained. It occurs dissolved in sea water and in most mineral waters. It also occurs in nature in association with minerals such as epsomite, gypsum, and limestone.

As a white powder, epsom salt is used as a laxative. Epsom salt can prevent the bowels (intestines) from absorbing water. Epsom salt should not be taken frequently. It interferes with the absorption of food materials. It should never be taken when there is abdominal pain.

Epsom salt is also mixed with water to make a solution for soaking inflamed body parts, especially the feet and hands.

J.J.A./A.D.

EQUATOR (i kwāt′ ər) The equator is an imaginary line around the middle of the earth, located halfway between the North and South Poles. The equator represents 0° latitude on a map. The equator is divided into 360° of longitude. (*See* LATITUDE AND LONGITUDE.)

Because of the slight bulge of the earth at the equator, the equatorial circumference (the length of the equator's circle) is a little longer than the polar circumference (the length of a circle around the earth which runs through both poles). At the equator, day and night are always 12 hours each.   J.M.C./W.R.S.

EQUILIBRIUM (ē′ kwə lib′ rē əm) Equilibrium is a state of rest or balance due to the equal action of opposing forces. When two or more forces acting on a body oppose or neutralize each other so that the body does not move, the forces are said to be in equilibrium. For example, at the exact time that the forward force of a football fullback is neutralized by the equal opposing force of a tackler, the forces are in equilibrium.

The ease with which the equilibrium of a body may be upset determines its type of equilibrium. If the center of gravity of an object must be raised in order to tilt it, the object is said to be in stable equilibrium. For example, a book lying on a table is in stable equilibrium. A pencil, balanced on a finger, is in unstable equilibrium. The slightest tipping of the pencil lowers its center of gravity, causing the knife to fall. A ball resting on a floor is in neutral equilibrium. Movements will neither raise nor lower its center of gravity.

A chemical equilibrium is a state of balance that is reached when chemical changes have apparently stopped. (*See* CHEMICAL REACTION.)   J.J.A./A.D.

EQUINOX (ē′ kwə näks′) The equinox is one of two days when the sun is directly over the equator at noon. The equinoxes usually occur on September 21 and March 21. On both these days, day and night are of equal length all over the world. The March 21 equinox is called the spring or vernal equinox because it signals the official start of spring in the northern hemisphere. September 21 is called the autumnal equinox because it is the first day of autumn in the northern hemisphere. *See also* SEASON; SOLSTICE.

J.M.C./C.R.

EQUIVALENT (i kwiv′ ə lənt) The equivalent of a substance is an important measurement. It tells a chemist how much of that substance will combine or react with a set amount of another substance. The equivalent is also called the equivalent weight. It can be measured in grams. This is the gram-equivalent.

The equivalent of a substance is the number of grams that will combine with or displace one gram of hydrogen or eight grams of oxygen. One gram-equivalent of a substance will react with one gram-equivalent of another substance, or with a simple multiple or fraction of that amount.

For an element, the equivalent weight is found by dividing its atomic weight by its valence. *See also* CENTIMETER-GRAM-SECOND SYSTEM.   D.M.H.W./A.D.

ERBIUM (ər′ bē əm) Erbium is a metallic element. It belongs to the group of elements called the rare earths. Its chemical symbol is Er. It has an atomic number of 68 and an atomic weight of 167.3. Erbium melts at about 1,500°C [2,732°F] and boils at 2,510°C [4,550°F]. It has a valence of three. It forms rose-colored salts. It was named for the town of Ytterby in Sweden. It was discovered there in 1843 by the Swedish chemist Carl Mosander. It is found in the minerals gadolinite and euxenite.   D.M.H.W./J.R.W.

ERG (ərg) An erg is a unit of work, or energy, in the centimeter-gram-second (cgs) system of units. It equals the work done by a force of 1 dyne acting over a distance of 1 cm

[0.4 in]. An erg is also equal to one ten-millionth of a joule.   W.R.P./R.W.L.

EROSION (i rō′ zhən) Erosion is the gradual wearing down and carrying away of the earth's materials. Natural or geological erosion is a slow process caused by the weather, oceans, running water, wind, and ice. Soil erosion is sometimes the result of the abuse of land by people. (*See* WEATHERING.)

In geological erosion, the weather plays a major role. The wind is constantly wearing away rock, especially in dry areas. In moist areas, water fills the cracks in rocks. If the temperature falls below the freezing point, 0°C [32°F], the water freezes. Since ice occupies more space than water, the rocks are broken apart by the expanding ice. This rock debris may fall down cliffs or mountainsides, forming the piles of rock often seen along the seashore. These piles are called talus or scree.

Water is another important factor in erosion. Rivers carry pebbles, sand, and other debris that constantly rub against the river bed. The Grand Canyon in Arizona is a result of the erosion caused by the Colorado River. Some of the material carried by a river is deposited at its mouth, forming a delta.

Glaciers carry material from one location to another. When the glaciers retreated during the last ice age, they made significant changes in the landscape of the northern hemisphere. (*See* GLACIATION.)

Ocean waves pounding against the coast are constantly changing the shoreline. In some places, waves batter and erode the land. In other places, the eroded material is deposited to form new land.

Soil erosion may occur because people change the land, making it much more vulnerable to geological erosion. Natural vegetation, like forests and grasslands, holds the soil securely in place. When the vegetation is removed, the soil can be washed away by a heavy rainfall. Farm land is subject to severe erosion, especially in times of drought. *See also* GEOMORPHOLOGY.   J.M.C./W.R.S.

Sea erosion can sometimes wear even hard rock into strange shapes. Below, the Old Man of Hoy, a thin column of rock in the Orkney islands, Scotland, is the result of erosion. Erosion like this is a very slow process.

ESCALATOR (es′ kə lāt′ ər) An escalator is a moving stairway used in large stores and public buildings, like railroad, bus, and airline terminals. Passengers stand on steps mounted on an endless belt. The belt is driven by an electric motor. (*See* CONVEYOR.) The passengers are carried either up or down depending upon the direction the escalator is running. Escalators usually operate at a speed of about 0.61 m [2 ft] per second. At the top and the bottom, the steps fold to make a flat, moving platform which is level with the landing. This allows the passengers to step on and off the escalator easily. Moving handrails are on either side of the steps. They are usually made of rubber and canvas. The handrails move at the same speed as the steps.

An escalator can handle about ten times the hourly capacity of an average elevator. The first escalator was displayed in 1900 at the Paris Exposition by the Otis Elevator Company. In 1901, this machine was reinstalled at the Gimbel Brothers department store in Philadelphia, and was used until 1939.

W.R.P./R.W.L.

ESOPHAGUS (i säf′ ə gəs) The esophagus, or gullet, is a muscular tube in vertebrates that leads from the back of the mouth (pharynx) to the stomach. It is part of the alimentary canal. The esophagus is made of bands of circular and longitudinal muscles which contract in waves to force food into the stomach. These waves are called peristalsis. Although both striated and smooth muscles make up the esophagus, control of peristalsis is involuntary.

The length of the esophagus varies from animal to animal. A fish has a very short esophagus, while the giraffe has a long one. The esophagus of the bird is modified with a saclike storage structure called a crop. The human esophagus is located behind the trachea and is about 30 cm [12 in] long and about 2.5 cm [1 in] in diameter. It is able to stretch, however, to allow the passage of large particles of food. There are special sphincter muscles at both ends of the esophagus. When food enters the mouth, it is mixed with saliva. The esophageal sphincter, located between the pharynx and the esophagus, opens, lets the food in, and closes again to keep the food from backing up into the mouth. Lubrication is added by mucus-secreting glands along the esophagus as peristalsis pushes the food through. The cardiac sphincter, located between the esophagus and the stomach, opens, letting food pass into the stomach. The sphincter then closes to prevent gastric fluids in the stomach from entering the esophagus. Heartburn is a condition caused by gastric juice in the esophagus.

Some animals, such as ruminants, are able to cause the esophagus to undergo a reverse peristalsis. This brings food from the stomach back up into the mouth. This returned food, or cud, is chewed and swallowed again.

A.J.C./J.J.F.

Left, the ester isoamyl acetate has the smell of bananas. Isoamyl acetate can be made synthetically to give banana flavor to ice cream and toothpaste, among other substances.

ESTER (es′ tər) Esters are a group of chemical compounds. They are formed by the reaction of an alcohol with an acid. Esters are organic chemicals. (*See* COMPOUND; ORGANIC CHEMISTRY.) All acids contain an acidic hydrogen atom. This atom can be replaced by a metal to form a salt. Or it can be replaced by an organic hydrocarbon group to form an ester.

An example of an ester is ethyl acetate. It is made by acetic acid reacting with ethanol.

Ethanol is an alcohol. It is also called ethyl alcohol. In ethyl acetate, the ethyl group replaces the acidic hydrogen in acetic acid.

Many esters have a pleasant odor. The flavor of fruits and the perfumes of flowers are caused mainly by esters. Esters are used as solvents and in manufacturing other chemicals. They are also used as artificial flavors and perfumes. M.E./J.M.

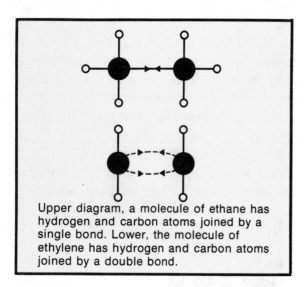

Upper diagram, a molecule of ethane has hydrogen and carbon atoms joined by a single bond. Lower, the molecule of ethylene has hydrogen and carbon atoms joined by a double bond.

ETHANE (eth′ ān′) Ethane (C_2H_6) is a colorless and odorless gas. It is found in natural gas and in coal gas. Its boiling point is −89°C [−128°F]. It is used in industry for making other chemical compounds. Ethane is a hydrocarbon because its molecule contains only hydrogen and carbon atoms. *See also* HYDROCARBON. M.E./J.M.

ETHER (ē′ thər) Ether ($C_2H_5OC_2H_5$) is a pleasant-smelling liquid. It boils at 34.5°C [94.1° F]. Its vapor is very flammable. Ether must, therefore, be handled very carefully and kept well away from flames. Ether is made by ethanol reacting with sulfuric acid. Ether is used as an anaesthetic. It is also widely used in industry for dissolving waxes, oils, and other products.

Chemists use the word ether to mean a group of chemical compounds. They call the ether described above diethyl ether. Ethers always have two hydrocarbon groups attached to an oxygen atom. M.E./J.M.

ETHYLENE (eth′ ə lēn′) Ethylene (C_2H_4) is a colorless gas with a faint smell resembling ether. It is made by removing some of the hydrogen from ethane. It is also obtained by refining petroleum. Ethylene is used as an anaesthetic, a fuel, and in making other chemicals. It also helps to ripen fruit. In a molecule of ethylene, the two carbon atoms are joined together by a double bond. (*See* BOND, CHEMICAL.) Its formula can be written as $CH_2{=}CH_2$.

A large amount of ethylene is used to make polyethylene. In order to make polyethylene, ethylene is polymerized. (*See* POLYMERIZATION.) This splits open the double bond, and long chains of CH_2 groups are formed. Chemists sometimes call ethylene ethene. M.E./J.M.

Above, an ethylene producing plant located in Grangemouth, Scotland.

EUCALYPTUS (yü′ kə lip′ təs) Eucalyptus is a genus with more than 500 species of tall, fast-growing trees. Native to Australia, these members of the myrtle family grow in warm, moist regions throughout the world. Some

Eucalyptus leaves and buds are the sole source of food of the koala bear.

species grow as tall as 100 m [330 ft]. The most common variety found in the United States is the blue gum eucalyptus (*Eucalyptus globulus*). This tree is cultivated in Florida, California, and Texas, and is frequently grown as a windbreaker around orchards of citrus trees. Like all eucalyptus, it has long, thick leaves and nectar-filled flowers which grow in the axils.

Eucalyptus is an important source of lumber and is used for telephone poles, ships, and railroad ties. The bark is a source of tannin which is used in some medicines, and of a resin called Botany Bay kino which can be used to protect wood from worms. The leaves are rich in an oil which can be used as a stimulant, a deodorant, and an antiseptic.

A.J.C./M.H.S.

EUROPIUM (yu̇ rō′ pē əm) Europium (Eu) is a silvery white metallic element. It has an atomic number of 63 and an atomic weight of 151.96. The melting point of europium is around 822°C [1,512°F]. Its boiling point is

1,597°C [2,907°F]. Its relative density is 5.3. It belongs to a group of metals with very similar properties, called the alkaline earths. Europium was first discovered in 1901 by the French chemist Eugène Demarçay. He named it after the continent of Europe.

Europium occurs in the minerals bastnaesite and monazite. These minerals also contain a number of other alkaline earth metals. Europium is used to make control rods for nuclear reactors. These rods are used to control the speed of the nuclear reaction. Compounds of europium are used in color television sets to produce the color red.

M.E./J.R.W.

EUTROPHICATION *See* SUCCESSION.

EVAPORATION (i vap′ ə rā′ shən) Evaporation occurs when a substance changes from a liquid or solid state into a vapor or gas. The form of a substance depends on the temperature or the amount of pressure it is subjected to. For example, water in a dish in a warm room may soon dry up. Wet clothes hung on a clothesline on a dry sunny day lose their moisture in a short time. Heat in the air changes the water in the dish and the clothes to water vapor. The warmer and drier the air, the more rapidly evaporation goes on.

Evaporation takes place from the surface of a liquid at any temperature. It also takes place from solids. Ice and snow send off vapor. This can be observed a day or two after a snowstorm. The snow disappears, even though the temperature has never gone above freezing. The water evaporates directly from the solid without first becoming a liquid. The formation of vapor in this way is called sublimation.

Evaporation in plants is called transpiration. Plants absorb moisture through their roots. They lose the moisture by evaporation through their leaves. The more leaf surface exposed, the more rapid the transpiration.

When a liquid evaporates from the surface of an object, that surface becomes much cooler because it requires heat to change a liquid into a vapor or gas. For example, sponging a fevered patient with alcohol reduces body temperature. Heat is drawn from the body by evaporation of the alcohol. In this sense, evaporation is a cooling process.

In some large areas, the process of evaporation is vital to plant and animal life. Water evaporates from oceans, rivers, the moist earth, or ponds and lakes and later falls as rain on these areas. (*See* CLOUD; RAIN.)

Other substances, such as ether and ammonia, evaporate much more rapidly than water. The rapid evaporation of liquid ammonia absorbs much heat. Thus liquid ammonia is used in refrigerators that operate on gas instead of electricity. *See also* VOLATILE LIQUID.

J.J.A./A.D.

The evening primrose is one of more than 500 species of flowering plants which belong to the evening primrose family. This family also includes the popular fuchsias.

EVENING PRIMROSE FAMILY (ēv′ ning prim′ rōz′) The evening primrose family includes more than 500 species of herbaceous plants and shrubs. They grow throughout North America and in parts of Europe. The most common evening primrose, *Oenothera biennis*, is a wild flower that grows as tall as 1.8 m [6 ft]. It has hairy, stalkless leaves measuring about 15 cm [6 in] long. The flowers are usually large, about 10 cm [4 in] wide, and may be bright yellow, white, or pink. *See also* FUCHSIA.

J.J.A./A.D.

The Norway spruce is a common evergreen which is often used as a Christmas tree.

EVERGREEN (ev′ ər grēn′) An evergreen is a tree or shrub that keeps its leaves throughout the year rather than losing them in autumn. Many evergreens in North America are conifers, like the pine tree. Their needlelike leaves can survive the cold winters, unlike the broad, thin leaves of deciduous trees. Some evergreens do not have needles. Their leaves are tough and leathery so that they can also survive in the cold. Although evergreens always have leaves, the leaves and needles do not live forever. Most die in a year but are replaced by others before they die. *See also* HEATH FAMILY. S.R.G./M.H.S.

EVOLUTION

Evolution (ev′ ə lü′ shən) is the process by which all living things on earth today descended from common ancestors that lived millions of years ago. According to the theory of evolution, plants and animals have changed, or evolved, in an orderly way, and continue to change even now.

History of the theories of evolution The idea of evolution was first suggested by the Greeks about 2,500 years ago. Aristotle proposed that there may have been a gradual development of various species over a period of thousands of years. The first modern attempts to explain evolution were made in the early 1700s by a French scientist, George Louis Buffon. Buffon suggested that perhaps the horse and the ass were related. His ideas caused a religious uproar because the theory at that time was that each species was created individually and that none was related to another. Buffon believed that evolution took place as a result of environmental pressures, such as climate. In 1794, Erasmus Darwin (grandfather of Charles Darwin) proposed a similar theory of evolution, adding that if an organism adapted to its environment, this adaptation, or acquired characteristic, could be passed on to future generations.

In 1809, Jean Lemarck published *Zoological Philosophy,* in which he agreed with the work of Buffon and Darwin, but added that adaptations were the results of needs of animals. For example, a monkey has a thumb because the thumb helps it climb in trees. He also proposed that if an organism does not use an organ or body structure, that structure will waste away and not be passed on to future generations. Lamarck was the first to explain systematically the process of evolution. Baron Cuvier, however, rejected the idea of evolution because he could not find any proof of intermediate creatures which lived between prehistoric (based on fossils) and current ones.

The major advances in evolutionary theory came about as a result of the work of Charles Darwin. Darwin formulated his theory in 1838, proposed it in 1858, and published it in 1859 as *The Origin of Species.* He believed that organisms evolve as a result of natural selection. In the early 1900s, when the rules of heredity became understood, thanks to the work of Gregor Mendel, a major obstacle to acceptance of Darwin's theory was overcome.

Darwin's ideas opposed those traditionally held by many religions. The controversy was intense for years, and even sparked the famous 1925 ''monkey trial'' in which a Tennessee schoolteacher was convicted of teaching evolution. This ruling banned the teaching of evolution in Tennessee. It

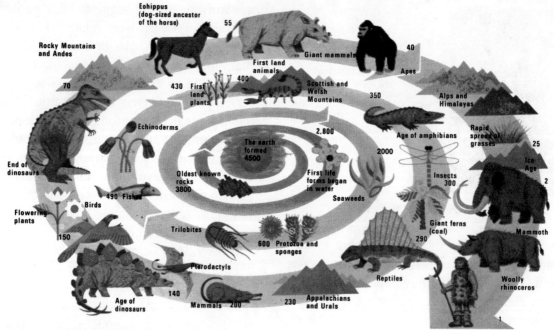

Evolution is shown here on a spiral time scale going back to the formation of the earth. The figures are in millions of years.

was not until 1968 that the United States Supreme Court ruled that anti-evolution laws were unconstitutional. Although scientists are in almost unanimous agreement that evolution is a fact, the religious-scientific controversy continues.

Evolution by natural selection   Darwin's theory of natural selection was based on several observations. He noted that no two living things were exactly alike. He also noted that living things reproduce at such a fast rate that, without controls, the earth would not be able to support all of them. Therefore, there is competition for the things (shelter, food, and so forth) necessary to live. Some organisms are better suited for this competition than others. For example, the peppered moth of Europe is a white moth with black speckling. This coloring enabled it to blend in with the bark of the trees on which it rested. Occasionally, a black peppered moth would appear, but was quickly preyed upon by birds because it lacked protective coloration. Then, about 100 years ago, increased industrial pollution

caused the tree trunks to turn black from soot. Thus, the black peppered moth blended with the tree trunks, while the white moths stood out, and were preyed upon. Today, there are few white peppered moths living in the industrialized areas of Europe. This change came about entirely through the action of natural selection, although people were responsible for changing the environment.

Genetics and evolution   The characteristics that are passed from one generation to the next are controlled by chromosomes and genes. Chromosomes are threadlike structures found in every living cell. Each chromosome has a number of genes arranged in a particular way. The genes determine how the cells of an organism develop. During sexual reproduction, genes from both parents are passed to the offspring. This results in new combinations of the genes, and may cause variations in size, color, or other characteristics of the organism. Because of natural selection, variations not useful to the organism die out. The remaining organisms are well adapted to their environment, and may pass useful variations to their offspring.

The speckled moth, lower in the picture (left) has evolved so that it is well camouflaged against the tree. The melanic moth, upper left, is normally found near industrial areas, where it has good camouflage against soot-covered buildings. Below, the placental mole (top) and the marsupial mole (bottom) look alike, but they have actually evolved in a similar way from different ancestors.

Mutations are changes that occur as the result of some gene combinations. Most mutations are harmful to the organism, and may even kill it. Occasionally, a mutation results in an advantageous variation. When this happens, the mutated organism may survive and pass on the variation to its offspring. It is thought that many new species started in this way.

Scientists generally agree that natural selection controls the results of inherited variations. An advantageous variation allows an organism to survive and flourish. At the same time it reduces the number of poorly adjusted plants and animals, which cannot compete as well.

Fossils and evolution   The history of life on earth is preserved in fossils. Fossils are evidence of ancient life. By studying them, scientists can observe the evolutionary changes that have occurred in organisms during the last 3.5 billion years.

Most fossils are preserved in layers of rock called strata. The fossils in the upper levels of strata tend to be similar to modern organisms, while those fossils in the lower strata often represent an earlier evolutionary stage of a modern organism. For example, a primitive fossil of a sea urchin with a shell was found in the bottom of a chalk deposit in England. As the scientists searched higher up in the deposit, they found sea urchin fossils of a more advanced evolutionary stage. At the uppermost strata, the organism had adapted to living without a shell. This example shows how fossils often form a series in strata, recording evolutionary stages.

The study of fossils is not nearly complete. There are many fossils that have not been found or studied yet. Nevertheless, a relationship has been established among the many forms of life, whose oldest fossils are amazingly similar.

Other evidence of evolution   The development of a human embryo parallels the evolution of man. The human embryo begins as a fertilized egg. (*See* REPRODUCTION.) It then develops gill-like structures, making possible its survival in the liquid environment within the mother. Soon, the embryo loses the gills and develops two lungs. The embryo's heart develops in several stages: The fish stage, the amphibian stage, and the reptilian stage. Eventually, the heart develops four chambers, and is prepared for life outside the mother.

Evidence of evolution can be seen when observing the bodies of animals. The arms of humans, the flippers of whales, and the wings of bats all show amazing similarity in their muscle and bone structure. These similarities indicate the possibility of a common ancestry.

There are many parts of the human body that no longer serve any purpose. These parts are called vestigial organs. People have about 180 vestigial organs. The appendix is such a leftover organ that no longer has a function in humans. It is, however, of great importance in plant-eating mammals, like the rabbit and the kangaroo. At some evolutionary stage, people must have needed the appendix, or it would never have developed.

Evolution and distribution of organisms Evidence of evolution is particularly apparent in isolated regions. Australia has a number of mammals that evolved in a different manner from the mammals of the larger continents. Millions of years ago, Australia separated from the major land mass, at a time when the mammals living there were rather primitive. (*See* CONTINENTAL DRIFT.) Mammals like the platypus and kangaroo thus followed unique evolutionary paths because of the absence of competition from the more highly evolved organisms living on other continents.

The Galápagos Islands in the Pacific Ocean are separated by the ocean from South America. It is here that Charles Darwin noticed that each island had distinct species of birds and reptiles. Each species had followed a slightly different evolutionary path from the mainland organisms. Thus the organisms on the Galápagos Islands evolved so as to suit the environment on each particular island, without significant influence from the mainland.

Today, it is evident that environment, natural selection, and genetics play major roles in evolution. There are probably other factors influencing evolution that have not yet been determined. The fossil record is incomplete, and there is still much to learn about genetics. Nevertheless, evolution is still the most plausible explanation for the development of the diversity of life on earth.

J.M.C./E.R.L.

The large shovel crane is loading earth and rock into a dump truck, which will remove it from the excavation site.

EXCAVATION (ek′ skə vā′ shən) Excavation is the removal of earth or rock from the ground. In the building of things such as bridges and large buildings, the civil engineer must be sure that the structure is erected on a firm foundation. Sometimes it is necessary to excavate down to bedrock. It could also mean excavating down sufficiently to make sure the foundation is bedded firmly in the ground.

In the building of tunnels, huge amounts of earth and rock must be excavated. Before strip mining of coal and ores can be performed, the excavation of the overlying earth, or overburden, must be done. Underwater excavation is carried out to deepen and clear navigation channels. (*See* DREDGING.)

Where large amounts of rock must be moved, explosives are used. Shot holes are drilled into the rock with pneumatic rock drills or jackhammers. The explosives are packed into them and fired. (*See* DRILLING.) This is the usual method of tunneling in hard rock. Tunneling in soft rock, such as clay, is carried out with a cutter. The cutter also acts as a protective shield for underground workers.

Most excavation takes place on the surface. Various machines have been developed to work with different situations. The biggest excavators are those used to strip the overburden off coal and ore deposits. A common machine used for this work is the dragline. This large machine, or excavator, has a bucket which is cast from a line extending from a boom. The bucket is dragged back along the ground. It scoops up soil and rock as it is being dragged.

When coal is excavated from an exposed seam, dipper shovels are used. In this type of excavator, the digging bucket is attached to a rigid arm and forced forward, or dragged backward, into the deposit.

Smaller types of excavators include the grab, in which a bucket is dropped from a height so that it penetrates the ground. The jaws are brought together and the bucket lifted.

Other excavators have a basic body structure made up of crawler tracks, turntable, cabin, and boom. They can be made into different types of excavators. This is done by fitting various attachments to the basic machine. These excavators can also be used as cranes and piling frames. (*See* PILING.)

For other jobs, such as digging trenches, bucket-type excavators are used. One kind has an endless chain on a boom, which is angled down into the ground. The excavated material is deposited onto a conveyor belt for removal. (*See* CONVEYOR.)   J.J.A./R.W.L.

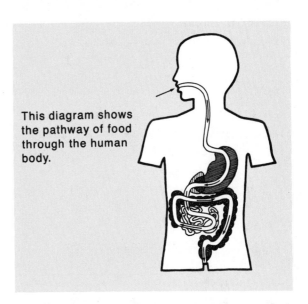

This diagram shows the pathway of food through the human body.

EXCRETION (ik skrē′ shən) Excretion is the process by which a living organism removes the waste products of metabolism from its body. When proteins are used (metabolized) by an organism, nitrogen-containing wastes such as ammonia, urea, and uric acid are produced. Since these wastes are poisonous, they must be removed from the body. Metabolism produces other wastes such as carbon dioxide and water which also must be removed from the body.

All animals produce metabolic wastes and must have a system for removing these wastes. Some simple Protista, such as the ameba and paramecium, allow wastes to diffuse across the body wall into the surrounding medium. (*See* DIFFUSION.) Many of these simple organisms accumulate wastes in spaces called contractile vacuoles which "squirt" the wastes out of the body. Most advanced animals have evolved an elaborate excretory system that filters wastes and foreign substances out of the blood. In vertebrates, the kidneys perform not only this function, but also help regulate the chemical composition of the blood by removing excess salts. All these wastes, along with excess water from the blood and body tissues, form urine which is stored in the bladder before being eliminated. Although many factors influence the amount and composition of urine, an average adult eliminates about 1 liter [30 fl oz] of urine per day.

The skin is another important organ of excretion. An average adult loses about 0.7 liters [24 fl oz] of water and a small amount of salt each day in perspiration. If the person is active or perspiring heavily, he loses much more. This excretion is controlled by the sweat glands and serves primarily to keep the body cool.

The lungs are also excretory organs because they get rid of carbon dioxide and water vapor. An average person gives off about 0.2 liters of carbon dioxide per minute. For some animals, such as dogs, the lungs are vital for temperature control. Although dogs have sweat glands, a healthy dog rarely perspires. Instead, it gets rid of excess moisture and cools itself off by panting, breathing heavily with its mouth open and its tongue out.

Some animals have other specialized excretory structures. Sea fishes excrete excess salt through their gills. The scales on the wings of butterflies and moths often contain excreted wastes. Insects use much of their nitrogen-containing wastes to build strong exoskeletons. (*See* SKELETON.) Insects also have specialized malpighian tubules which remove the wastes but recycle virtually all of the water.

Plants often handle wastes by converting them into oils or solids which are transported to the cells of the bark or leaves for storage. Substances commonly considered wastes, such as nitrogen-containing compounds, water, and carbon dioxide, are actually vital to a plant's growth. (*See* PHOTOSYNTHESIS.) *See also* FOOD CHAIN; NITROGEN CYCLE.

A.J.C./J.J.F.

EXOBIOLOGY (ek′ sō bī äl′ ə je) Exobiology is a branch of biology that deals with the search for and study of extraterrestrial life— life on other planets.

The question of life on other planets is an ancient one that has been argued by philosophers, scientists, writers, and religious scholars for thousands of years. Some contend that life does or may exist on other planets; others say no.

Physical and chemical processes occurred on earth 3.6 billion years ago, during its early formation, which gave rise to life forms as we know them. Fossil records, meteorites, and information gained from space probes and radio astronomy are examined by exobiologists for evidence that similar biological activity might have occurred on other planets.

Scientists have developed many instruments to learn about stars, planets, comets, asteroids, interstellar dust, and the moons of Jupiter and Saturn. Radio telescopes detect, collect, and record emissions and radiation received from distant galaxies and other sources in space. Space probes are sent into the universe to transmit photos and other information back to earth.

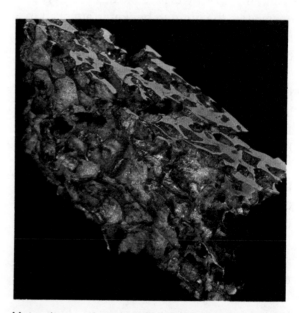

Meteorites such as this one have given exobiologists clues to the possible existence of other life.

Radio astronomers have detected complex molecules in the great clouds of gas and dust in interstellar space. Some are compounds of carbon, which may be forerunners of more complex molecules of living matter. It is possible that some of the molecules were part of the rocky debris that circulates in the solar system and falls to earth in meteorites.

Astrophysicists and exobiologists deal with many of the same questions about life. Some strongly advocate the possibility of extraterrestrial intelligence. They reason that if the conditions for life and the existence of intelligent beings arose in our solar system, then the same thing could have happened in another star system. In 1983, from infrared satellite observations, astronomers discovered that a star called Vega has a solar system. Thus Vega is now the only star besides our sun known to have satellites. Like the planets of our solar system, whatever is in orbit around Vega must be considered as a possible site for life to have formed.

Below is an artist's conception — based on scientific facts — of some of the kinds of creatures that would live on a planet that had a very wet environment.

Other scientists state that extraterrestrial beings do not exist. They suggest that earth is the only planet in the entire universe where intelligent life forms exist.

The NASA space program has concerned itself with the search for information about space. NASA has sent Viking, Pioneer, and Voyager satellites into space. The Apollo astronauts brought back ancient rocks from the moon. But space travel to the nearest star is well beyond our technological capabilities at this time.

For hundreds of years, people thought that life existed on Mars, the red planet. Two Viking space probes landed on Mars in 1976 and conducted experiments. Nothing was found that proved that microbes (microorganisms) or any life forms exist on Mars.

The Voyager space probes revealed traces of water, ammonia, methane, and other organic compounds in Jupiter's atmosphere. They also showed that the orange haze surrounding Saturn's largest moon, Titan, is a nitrogen atmosphere in which complex organic molecules could have formed. *See also* COSMOLOGY; JUPITER; SATURN.   D.A.T./G.D.B.

EXOTHERMIC REACTION (ek' sō thər' mik rē ak' shən) In a chemical reaction, the compounds involved sometimes give off heat. (*See* COMPOUND.) When this happens, the reaction is called an exothermic reaction. The opposite can also happen. The compounds can become colder and absorb heat from their surroundings. This is called an endothermic reaction. In an exothermic reaction, the reacting compounds contain more energy than the products. As the reaction takes place, the extra energy is given off as heat.

A common example of an exothermic reaction is the burning of a fuel such as natural gas. Natural gas is a mixture of hydrocarbons. These react with the oxygen in the air to form carbon dioxide and water vapor. Both carbon dioxide and water are very stable compounds because they have a low energy content. Natural gas and oxygen have a higher energy content. When the fuel burns, only part of this energy goes into the carbon dioxide and water. The rest is given off as heat. M.E./A.D.

EXPANSION (ik span' chən) Expansion is a process whereby a body increases in volume while keeping the same mass. In other words, the size of a body increases without the addition of more material to the body. The term is often used in connection with the heating of a material. Most solids and liquids expand when heated. Heat causes expansion because it increases the vibrations of a material's atoms or molecules. The increased vibrations force the atoms or molecules apart. Therefore the body becomes larger. The process of melting is an extension of the expansion process in solids. Eventually, all the atoms or molecules move about so rapidly that they overcome the forces that bind them together.

Different materials expand by different amounts when their temperature is raised by one degree. For example, aluminum expands twice as much as iron under the same temperature increase.

Gases also expand when heated at a constant pressure. If a gas is heated in a container that prevents expansion, the pressure of the gas increases. (*See* GAS; PRESSURE.) *See also* STATES OF MATTER. J.J.A./J.T.

EXPLOSIVE (ik splō' siv) An explosive is a substance that bursts violently when acted upon by a strong blow or by heat. When such a substance explodes, its solids and liquids change to gases and produce great amounts of heat. The hot gases expand violently. They need more space than the original solids and liquids. The gases expand to volumes hundreds of times as big as the explosive. They travel outward at an extremely high speed. The high speed causes explosives to have much force.

Most of the useful explosives contain the chemical elements carbon, nitrogen, hydrogen, and oxygen. Common gases formed in an explosion are carbon dioxide, steam, and nitrogen.

There are three main types of explosives. One type consists of mechanical explosives. Cardox is a mechanical explosive. Cardox is made up of a sealed metal tube filled with liquid carbon dioxide and a means of heating the tube. Heat causes the liquid to become a gas that bursts the seal and expands rapidly. Cardox is a slow, low-powered explosive. It is used in mines to split rock.

A second group of explosives is known as chemical explosives. The two kinds of chemical explosives are low explosives and high explosives. A low explosive burns very rapidly after it is set on fire. It explodes only when enclosed in a strong container. Otherwise, it simply burns in a flash. A large amount of gas results from burning a low explosive. The gas produces waves of very high pressure, or shock waves, within the container. The gas bursts the container and

Explosives (facing right) are sometimes used to save time in demolition projects.

makes an explosion. Gunpowder is a low explosive used to push bullets out of guns. When gunpowder burns, it gives off large amounts of gases. These gases produce the force of the explosion. Inside a closed container, such as a shell, the gases create great forces which shatter the shell. The blast of the explosion is the hot escaping gases, together with bits of material from the shell. Gunpowder is a mixture of chemicals which burn rapidly. In order to burn, however, gunpowder needs oxygen. Gunpowder gets its oxygen from potassium nitrate, one of its chemicals. Potassium nitrate is a chemical compound which gives up oxygen easily. Potassium nitrate is therefore described as being an oxidizing compound. This oxygen supply enables gunpowder to burn even inside a closed container, where there is little or no air. The rate of detonation in gunpowder may range from 0.9 to 91 m [3 to 300 ft] per second, depending on the pressure surrounding the explosive. The rate of detonation is the speed at which the explosion moves through the explosive.

A high explosive is one in which heat and gas are produced by a very fast chemical reaction. The rate of detonation in high explosives can be as fast as 6 km [4 mi] per second. This reaction may be started by a shock caused by striking the explosive. Or it may be started by the shock of a small explosion in a device that is very sensitive to heat or impact. The device is called a detonator. Blasting caps are detonators that explode and then cause dynamite to explode. High explosives generally expand faster and are more powerful than low explosives. High explosives are used where great shattering force is needed, as in bombs and in explosives used to blast rock. Trinitrotoluene, or TNT, picric acid (PETN), nitroglycerine, and RDX are high explosives. Such explosives cannot be used in guns. The suddenness of the explosion would blow the gun apart.

The third main of type of explosives is nuclear explosives. Nuclear explosives depend on the enormous temperature of millions of degrees. The temperature is produced by either nuclear fission or nuclear fusion. The heat produced expands the surrounding air with extreme speed, giving it explosive force. The atomic bomb explodes by fission. The hydrogen bomb explodes by fusion.

Nuclear explosives are the most powerful explosives. In such explosives, vast amounts of gas, heat, and light are given off. Also, large amounts of radioactive matter are formed. This matter, which reaches the ground as radioactive fallout, is more dangerous to people than the actual explosion.

Explosives are used in almost all weapons of war. But many kinds of explosives are used in other activities, such as in blasting rock mines, building dams, and breaking up ice blocks in rivers. J.J.A./J.M.

EXPONENT (ik spō′ nənt) In mathematics, such as algebra, the operation of multiplying a number by itself is shown by an exponent. The exponent is a small number to the right and toward the top of the base number. For example, the number 4 multiplied by itself 3 times is written as 4^3, where 4 is the base number and 3 is the exponent.

There are five basic laws of exponents. The law of exponents for multiplication states that 2 or more powers having the same base number may be multiplied by adding the exponents and raising the common base to that power. For example,

$$6^2 \times 6^3 = 6^{2+3} = 6^5$$

Dividing powers of the same base is done by subtracting exponents:

$$4^4 \div 4^2 = 4^{4-2} = 4^2$$

To raise a power to a power, multiply the exponents:

$$(2^3)^2 = 2^{3\times2} = 2^6$$

The fourth law of exponents states that the power of a product is equal to the product of the powers of the factors:

$$(2 \times 3^2 \times 5^3)^2 = 2^{(1) \times 2} \times 3^{2 \times 2} \times 5^{3 \times 2} = 2^2 \times 3^4 \times 5^6$$

The fifth law of exponents states that the power of a quotient is equal to the quotient of each number raised to that power:

$$\left(\frac{3}{4}\right)^3 = \frac{3^3}{4^3}$$

Some exponents need a special explanation. Zero exponents arise in division of powers:

$$4^3 \div 4^3 = 4^0$$

The term "zero power" may seem meaningless. But since any number divided by itself equals 1, $4^3 \div 4^3$ must equal 1. Therefore 4^0 also equals 1. The zero power of any number except zero is equal to 1. In a similar way, the "first power" of any number must be the number itself. In other words, every number written without an exponent carries the exponent 1 understood. A number with a negative exponent is equal to 1 divided by the same number with the corresponding positive exponent:

$$8^{-2} = \frac{1}{8^2}$$

Fractional exponents indicate roots:

$$9^{\frac{1}{2}} = \sqrt{9}$$

(*See* ROOT, MATHEMATICAL.)   J.J.A./S.P.A.

EXPOSURE METER (ik spō′ zhər mēt′ ər) An exposure meter is a device used in photography to measure the brightness of light. It enables the photographer to adjust the lens on the camera so that the film receives the proper amount of light for a perfect exposure. Some cameras have built-in exposure meters that set the lens openings automatically. Other built-in meters simply indicate the proper setting, and the photographer makes the change manually.

Exposure meters measure the amount of light reflected from the subject, or the light falling on the subject. They do this by a photoelectric process. The light enters the meter and falls on a photo cell. The photo cell is a small iron plate coated with selenium, a non-metallic element that is electrically sensitive to light. The selenium, in turn, is coated with a 0.00001 mm [0.0000004 in] layer of platinum. The platinum is so thin that it is almost transparent. Light passes through it and strikes the selenium. This causes electrons in the selenium to flow in an electrical circuit through the platinum to the iron. The very weak current produced in this manner is measured with a sensitive electric meter, and displayed by a moving pointer on a scale. The readings are given in different lens settings, or f-stops.

Another type of exposure meter uses a cadmium sulfide cell that is sensitive to light. The cell controls electric current supplied by a battery. The amount of electric current the cell allows to pass depends upon the amount of light that shines on the cell. The current that passes through the cell is measured by an electric meter and displayed by a pointer on a scale. Exposure meters of this type are very responsive to weak light conditions, such as moonlight.

A photometer is an exposure meter that measures the strength of light by comparing it to another light of known strength. This type of exposure meter is not used as widely as the photoelectric type because it is more complicated to operate. *See also* CAMERA; LIGHT.

W.R.P./S.S.B.

EXTRASENSORY PERCEPTION (ek′ strə sens′ ə rē pər sep′ shən) Extrasensory perception describes a way of being aware of something without the use of the known senses. The known senses are sight, hearing, smell, touch, and taste. For instance, knowing what a person is going to say before he says it is an example of extrasensory perception. Extrasensory perception is often abbreviated ESP.

There is much debate over whether or not extrasensory perception exists. If it does exist, the way it works is unknown. Most scientists believe that it is best to think of ESP as something that might be true but has not been proved.

There are four basic areas in the field of extrasensory perception. Telepathy is sometimes called ''mind reading.'' It is the sending of thoughts, feelings, or knowledge from one person to another in some unknown way. For instance, if a person wants someone to call on the telephone, the person may sit and concentrate about that wish. Somehow, the other person ''receives'' the message and makes the telephone call. Clairvoyance is being mentally aware of something, such as an event or a person, without the use of the known senses, and without the telepathic help of another person. A person in New York may be aware that someone in Chicago is very ill, but he or she has found this out in a way other than the known ways of finding things out. Precognition is knowledge of an event before it happens by means of telepathy or clairvoyance. Psychokinesis is the psychological control of physical objects. For example, a person concentrating for ''heads'' to show on the flip of a coin can influence ''heads'' to appear.

For centuries, certain people have claimed extrasensory abilities. Some believed they knew the future. Others thought they could talk with ghosts or spirits. Others thought they could read minds. In 1882, a group of men met in London and formed the Society for Psychical Research. They set out to apply science in investigating claims of extrasensory perception. Since then, others have tried to do the same thing. No one has ever found the claims to be altogether true. Research into ESP continues.

In the United States, one of the most noted ESP researchers was J. B. Rhine. For many years, he headed a research program for ESP at Duke University in North Carolina. He and his co-workers did much work on telepathy. The ESP researchers used a deck of 25 cards with certain symbols, or signs, on them. Dr. Rhine claimed that many persons can tell what is on the cards even though these persons cannot see them. He said that the scores they make in telling what is on the cards are better than they would make in just guessing. Other researchers say that Dr. Rhine's experiments were not done scientifically, and therefore his results do not prove that ESP exists.

If extrasensory perception is assumed to exist, it is clear that people vary widely in ESP capacity. Also, ESP abilities come and go. A person may show positive ESP results in the early stages of an experiment but show chance results later. It has also been suggested that a person may have special ESP abilities for a limited period in his life and not at any other time.

The debate over the existence of ESP will no doubt continue until there is reasonable and believable evidence explaining how this form of awareness and communication is possible.

Scientists study ESP because if one or a few people were found to possess these abilities, the importance of ESP could be enormous. For example, a person with ESP abilities might be able to predict future wars, locate valuable mineral deposits, and accomplish other things of great importance. The fact that nobody has been found who can do such things raises the question of whether or not ESP is an unqualified fact.   J.J.A./J.J.F.

Synthetic fibers are made by a special kind of extrusion process. Above, cellulose acetate is extruded through a spinneret to make synthetic fibers.

EXTRUSION (ik strü′ zhən) Extrusion is a process used to shape metals and plastics into pipes, tubes, sheets, and other long lengths. Extruded materials may be of various cross-sections, such as square or round. Extrusion is also used to coat wires and cables with either metal or plastic. The process consists of forcing softened or molten material through an opening. The opening is part of a die. It has about the same diameter as the finished product. In the extrusion of metals, there are three basic processes.

The direct process is the most widely used method of extrusion. In this process, a ram in one end of the cylinder pushes against a billet, which is a short piece of metal. The ram forces the metal through a die opening at the other end of the cylinder. The metal flows out of the cylinder like toothpaste out of a tube.

The hydrostatic process is similar to the direct method. But in the hydrostatic process, fluid, such as castor oil, surrounds the billet. The ram pushes on the fluid. The fluid pressure forces the metal through the die opening.

The indirect process uses a die and a hollow ram. They push a billet against the closed end of a cylinder and force the metal out of the cylinder through the die opening and the ram.

Most extrusion methods shape metals that have been heated. Heat increases the flexibility of a metal. The temperature of billets may range from 204°C [400°F] to more than 2204°C [4000°F]. Usually, the billet and die are coated with a lubricant to help the metal flow smoothly through the opening.

Cold extrusions are methods that shape metal at room temperature. One type of cold extrusion, called the Hooker method, is a direct process. Another kind, called impact extrusion, is an indirect process. More pressure is needed to shape cold metal than hot metal. Cold extrusion products have greater strength than heated extrusion products.

Plastics extrusion is similar in principle. Molten plastics, however, are at a much lower temperature than molten metals, and so the machinery is slightly different. The extrusion machine has a screwlike auger to force the molten plastic through the die hole. (*See* DRILLING.) The process of making synthetic fibers is a special kind of extrusion process. Molten plastic is forced through the many holes of a spinneret into air or a chemical solution. (*See* FIBER.)   J.J.A./J.T.

EYE AND VISION

The eyes (īz) are the sense organs that give human beings and most other animals the most accurate and detailed information about their surroundings. Most animals have eyes or similar, light-sensitive organs. Even one-celled animals will react to bright light. (*See* PROTISTA.) Some invertebrates, such as starfish and jellyfish, have pigmented spots that are light-sensitive. Spiders, snails, and some insects have simple eyes called ocelli with hard, fixed lenses that cannot focus. Organisms with these simple eyes can see light and some movement, but are unable to form a clear image. Many insects and crustaceans have compound eyes made of thousands of lenses joined together. Compound eyes can form hazy images, and they are especially good for detecting movement. Lobsters have compound eyes at the ends of movable stalks.

Squids and octopuses have eyes and vision (vizh′ ən) much like those of human beings and other vertebrates. They are able to focus and form clear images. Vertebrate eyes are usually adapted to fit an animal's life style. Many animals have a third eyelid, or

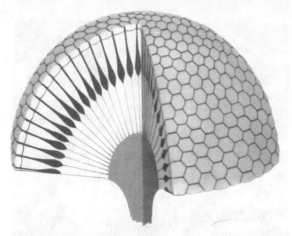

Above, the compound eye of insects has hundreds of small units, each of which has a lens and opaque pigment. In daylight the pigment extends from the lens to the retina, so that light enters each unit separately and cannot pass between them, as shown above. Each unit thus "sees" a separate image and the compound eye sees a mosaic of images.

Below, the head of a horsefly showing its compound eyes, typical of most insects.

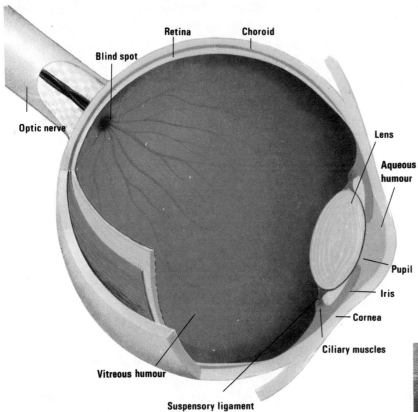

Retina   Choroid
Blind spot
Optic nerve
Lens
Aqueous humour
Pupil
Iris
Cornea
Ciliary muscles
Vitreous humour
Suspensory ligament

Left, a half-section of the human eye (seen in the photo below), showing its parts. The wall consists of three layers: the sclerotic, which is a tough outer membrane, the choroid, which is a soft brown layer containing the blood vessels, and the retina, which is the light-sensitive part of the eye. Nerves and blood vessels from the retina join to form the optic nerve and the point where they leave the eye is called the blind spot. Light entering the eye is refracted (bent) by the cornea, aqueous humor, lens, and vitreous humor, and is finally focused on the retina. The shape of the lens can be changed to allow the eye to focus on objects.

nictitating membrane, to protect the eye from dust or wind. Since fish live in the water, they have no need for eyelids or tearproducing glands. One kind of fish, the anableps, has eyes which can see above the water and below the water at the same time. The eagle with its large eyes has the keenest vision of any animal. Many nocturnal animals have large eyes to help them see in the semidarkness. (*See* NOCTURNAL HABIT.) Some cave-dwelling animals and some deep sea fish have tiny eyes that may be useless in the total darkness in which they live.

The human eye The human eye is a sphere measuring about 2.5 cm [1 in] in diameter. It rests in the orbit, a bony socket in the skull, and can move in all directions due to the actions of the six ocular muscles. The wall of the eyeball has three layers: the sclera, the middle layer, and the retina.

The sclera is the outermost layer and is made of tough, fibrous tissue. In the front of the eye, the sclera becomes the transparent cornea. The cornea is clear so that light can enter the eye. The cornea is about 13 mm [0.5 in] in diameter. Just behind the cornea is the anterior chamber which is filled with a watery fluid called aqueous humor. The aqueous humor helps the eye keep its shape and transports nutrients throughout the anterior chamber.

The middle layer includes the iris, the ciliary muscle, and the choroid. The iris is the colored part of the eye (usually brown or blue) located just inside the cornea. The iris surrounds the pupil, the hole through which light enters the eyeball. The pupil looks like a black circle in the middle of the front of the eye. There are muscles in the iris which can increase the size of the pupil to let more light in or decrease its size to let less light in. The ciliary muscle is part of the choroid and is attached to the lens. The ciliary muscle controls the shape of the lens to allow the eye to focus on near or distant objects. The choroid surrounds the eyeball just inside the sclera. The choroid is rich in blood vessels.

The retina is the innermost layer of the eye, located just inside the choroid. The retina contains light-sensitive cells with about 130,000,000 nerve endings. These connect to the brain by means of the optic nerve. These cells are either rods or cones, and are named for their appearance. Rods are located throughout the retina and are sensitive to dim light. The rods function primarily for night vision. The cones are centralized in the rear of the retina in a small area called the macula. Cones are sensitive to bright light, produce sharp images, and are responsible for color vision. The large space enclosed by the retina and the lens is called the posterior chamber and is filled with the clear, jellylike vitreous humor. The vitreous humor gives the eye its shape and transports nutrients throughout the posterior chamber.

The eyeball is protected by the eyebrows, eyelashes, and eyelids. All three function to keep dust and other irritants out of the eye, and also help limit the amount of bright light to which the eye is exposed. Each eyelid has three parts: the skin, the muscles controlling the skin, and the conjunctiva. The conjunctiva is a thin membrane lining the inside of the lid and part of the eyeball. It is kept moist by a constant stream of fluid—tears—produced by the lachrymal or tear glands. Blinking, or closing the eyelids, moistens and cleans the surface of the cornea.

How the eye sees   Vision, the ability to see, has four main stages. First, light rays from an object enter the pupil. Second, these rays are focused by the lens onto the retina. Third, the nerve endings in the rods and cones are stimulated and send a message through the optic nerve to the brain. Fourth, the brain interprets the nerve signals from the optic nerve, and "sees" the image formed in the eye.

Before light enters the pupil, it passes through the cornea and aqueous humor, causing it to bend slightly. (*See* REFRACTION.) The pupil is widened or narrowed to allow the proper amount of light to enter. As light rays travel through the lens, they are refracted even further so that they will focus on the retina. The lens changes shape in a process called accomodation to control this focusing. Because the lens can only focus on one object at a time, objects at different distances may appear to be blurred. A good example of this can be shown by looking at a tree through a screen door. If a person focuses on the tree, the screen will be blurred, whereas if he focuses on the screen, the tree will be blurred.

Each eye sends "image signals" to the brain by means of the optic nerves. These nerves pass through a nerve junction called the optic chiasma, where the "image signals" are combined. By comparing these two, slightly different images, the brain is able to perceive depth and distance. The ability of the brain to form one image from the images of two eyes is called binocular vision.

The spot where the optic nerve attaches to the retina has no rods or cones. As a result, this spot is not light-sensitive and is called the blind spot. If the image of an object is focused on the blind spot, the object will seem to be invisible.

Defects of the eye   Defects of the eye may be hereditary, or may be caused by other factors, such as age. With the exception of color blindness, most can be treated with corrective glasses or contact lenses.

Color blindness is an inherited defect in the cones which prevents a person from being able to distinguish differences between certain colors. Strabismus, or cross-eyes, is caused by an imbalance in the ocular muscles. As a result, the eyes turn inward or outward. This is a common condition in children that requires surgery only in severe cases. Astigmatism is blurring or distortion of vision due

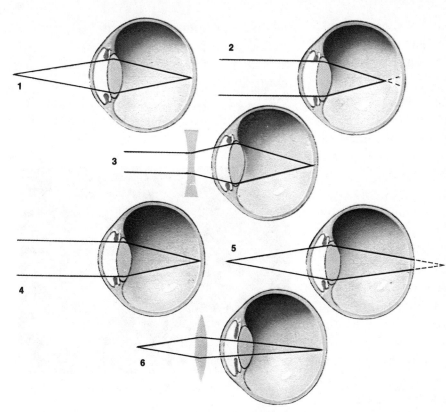

Defects of the eye. Myopia can be caused by distortion of the retina. 1. A near object can give a clear image to the myopic eye. 2. For distance viewing, the myopic eye has a blurred image because the light is brought into focus before the retina. 3. A diverging lens corrects the defect. Hyperopia, or farsightedness, is caused by an eyeball that is shorter than normal. 4. A distant object gives a clear image to the farsighted. 5. For a near object, the farsighted eye focuses the light behind the retina, giving a blurred image. 6. A converging lens corrects the defect.

to a defect in the shape of the cornea or lens. Presbyopia is the loss of accomodation, or ability to focus, as a result of hardening of the lens. Most people become somewhat presbyopic as they grow older.

Myopia, or nearsightedness, is caused by an eyeball which is longer than normal. As a result, the image is focused in front of, instead of on, the retina. Corrective glasses with concave lenses help treat this defect. Hyperopia, or farsightedness, is caused by an eyeball which is shorter than normal. As a result, the image is focused behind the retina. Corrective lenses with convex (curved outward) lenses help treat this defect.

Diseases of the eye Conjunctivitis is an inflammation of the conjunctiva of the eyelids and eyeball. Its mild form is called pink eye, and may be caused by allergies, irritation, or infections. A viral form of conjunctivitis, trachoma, is the major cause of blindness in Europe and Asia. (*See* VIRUS.)

A sty is an infection of a gland at the corner of the eyelid. A cataract is a condition in which the lens becomes cloudy or opaque, reducing the amount of light that enters the eye. Treatment may involve surgical removal of the lens and either implantation of an artificial lens or the use of special corrective glasses.

Glaucoma is increased pressure within the eyeball which puts pressure on, and eventually destroys, the optic nerve. Nightblindness is caused by a deficiency of vitamin A which results in damage to the rods. In a retinal detachment, the retina separates from the choroid and floats in the vitreous humor. This can be caused by a fall, a blow to the head, or by any other trauma to the eye. It is treated surgically and, in many cases, laser beams are used to fix the retina back in place. A corneal abrasion is a very painful scratch on the surface of the cornea. It usually heals with no ill effects. Corneal scarring, however, results from more severe injury or disease. Since the scar interferes with or totally obscures vision, the cornea may be removed and replaced with one from a donor. (*See* TRANSPLANTION.)

Eye specialists Healthy persons should have their eyes examined by a specialist every one or two years. These regular examinations help keep the eyes healthy by detecting diseases or disorders. Ophthalmology is the study of the eye, eye disorders, and eye diseases. An ophthalmologist is a medical doctor who specializes in treating disorders and diseases of the eye. An ophthalmologist can also check a patient's vision and prescribe corrective glasses or contact lenses. An ophthalmoscope is a special instrument that lets a doctor see into the eyeball to examine the blood vessels and the optic nerve. Many diseases which affect other parts of the body also cause changes in the eye. Diseases such as multiple sclerosis can sometimes be detected by an eye examination long before any symptoms appear.

An optometrist can test a person's vision and prescribe corrective glasses. An optician can make corrective glasses or contact lenses according to the prescription of an optometrist or an ophthalmologist. Although all these specialties are related, only the ophthalmologist is able to use medication or surgery to treat a disease of the eye.   A.J.C./J.J.F.

FAHRENHEIT SCALE (far′ ən hīt′ skāl′) The Fahrenheit scale of temperature is based on 32°F as the freezing point of water and 212°F as the boiling point of water. There are 180 units between the two points. The Fahrenheit scale was developed in the early 1700s by Gabriel Fahrenheit, a German physicist. The Fahrenheit scale is slowly being replaced by the Celsius scale in which the freezing point of water is 0°C, and the boiling point is 100°C.

The formula for converting Fahrenheit temperature to Celsius temperature is: $°C = 5/9(°F - 32°)$. The formula for converting Celsius temperature to Fahrenheit temperature is: $°F = 9/5(°C) + 32°$.   W.R.P./R.W.L.

Fairy shrimp grow to about one inch in length.

FAIRY SHRIMP (far′ ē shrimp) Fairy shrimp are small, primitive crustaceans which are almost transparent. They swim upside down by waving their many leaflike legs. These legs, which are fringed with bristles, also trap food particles and extract oxygen from the water. (*See* GILL.)

Fairy shrimp may suddenly appear in vast numbers, even in temporary pools. This is because they have very tough eggs. These eggs live in dried mud. They can also blow about in the wind. A very similar creature, called the brine shrimp, lives in salt lakes throughout the world.   J.J.A./C.S.H.

FALCON (fal′ kən) A falcon is a bird of prey that belongs to the family Falconidae. It is streamlined with a narrow tail and pointed wings. Falcons are able to fly extremely fast. Some species can travel over 160 km/hr [100 mi/hr]. This great speed allows them to catch other birds, rodents, and insects, all of which they eat.

Facing right, a young cuckoo falcon.

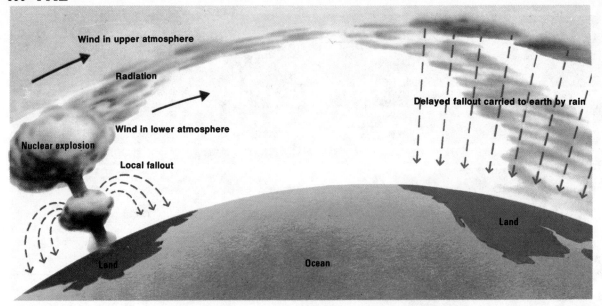

Wind in upper atmosphere

Radiation

Wind in lower atmosphere

Nuclear explosion

Local fallout

Delayed fallout carried to earth by rain

Land

Ocean

Land

There are six species of falcons in North America. Perhaps the best known is the peregrine falcon, one of the fastest birds in the world. This bird has been widely used in the sport of falconry. It is found all over the world. The peregrine falcon is now a rare and endangered species in most parts of North America. It is most numerous in the Arctic. The widespread use of pesticides has resulted in the poisoning of the bird and has caused its numbers to decrease. Ornithologists (scientists who study birds) are now working to restore the pregrine falcon to many areas. *See* ORNITHOLOGY.   S.R.G./L.L.S.

FALLOUT (fȯ′ laȯt′) Fallout is radioactive material that settles to the ground following a nuclear explosion. (*See* RADIOACTIVITY.) A great deal of intensely radioactive material is produced during a nuclear bomb explosion. (*See* NUCLEAR WEAPON.) This material combines with dust and moisture drawn up into the mushroom-shaped cloud, which forms after the explosion. The radioactive matter is carried by the wind until it returns to the earth as fallout. There are two types of fallout: local fallout and distant fallout.

Local fallout consists of heavy particles of intense radioactivity which reach the ground

After a nuclear explosion, heavy particles of atomic radiation fall on a wide area around the site of the explosion. Lighter particles rise into the upper atmosphere and may be carried long distances by the wind.

within a few hundred kilometers of the bomb site. Local fallout decreases in radioactivity as the distance from the bomb site increases. Severe illness or death may result from exposure to local fallout.

Distant fallout consists of fine radioactive particles carried by winds high in the atmosphere. These particles may circle the entire earth before reaching the ground through rain, snow, or fog. Distant fallout is less dangerous than local fallout, but may cause long term effects.

Fallout is extremely dangerous to all living things because of the radioactive isotopes it contains. The isotopes usually lose their radioactivity within a few hours or days of the explosion, but a few retain their radioactivity for several years. Fallout may cause cancer, radiation sickness, and severe genetic problems. (*See* GENETICS.) Protection from fallout may be sought in underground chambers called fallout shelters.   J.M.C./A.D.

FALSE SCORPION (fȯls′ skȯr′ pē ən) The false scorpions are tiny arachnids only 1 to 7.5

mm [0.04 to 0.3 in] long. They have four pairs of legs, and are armed with a pair of pincers (claws), often as long as their entire body.

False scorpions are found in most places with warm climates. They live under rocks, in books, and in old chests. They feed on carpet beetles, larvae, moths, bed bugs, and book lice. J.M.C./R.J.B.

FAMILY (fam′ lē) A family, in the classification of living organisms, is a group of closely related members of an order. The plants or animals in a family are not as closely related as those in a genus, however.

A.J.C./E.R.L.

FARAD (far′ ad′) A farad is a unit that measures the capacitance of a capacitor. A capacitor is a device used in electrical circuits. It is made of two parallel metal plates, placed close to each other but not touching. One plate has a positive electric charge and the other a negative charge of the same size. This produces a potential difference across the plates. (*See* CAPACITOR AND CAPACITANCE; POTENTIAL.) The potential difference is proportional to the size of the charge. This means that if the charge is doubled, then so is the potential difference. The capacitance of the device is equal to the charge divided by the potential difference. The capacitance is measured in farads, the charge is measured in coulombs, and the potential difference in volts. If a charge of one coulomb produces a potential difference of one volt, the capacitance is one farad.

The farad is a very large unit. Usually the microfarad or the picofarad are used instead. A microfarad is equal to a millionth of a farad. A picofarad is equal to millionth of a microfarad. *See also* METER-KILOGRAM-SECOND SYSTEM. M.E./R.W.L.

FARADAY, MICHAEL (1791–1867) Michael Faraday (far′ ə dā) was a British physicist and chemist. He made many important discoveries. In 1813, when he was a young man, he became assistant to Sir Humphrey Davy at the Royal Institution in London. He was made a professor in 1833 and worked there for the rest of his life. Hans Oersted discovered in 1820 than an electric current created a magnetic field. Faraday heard about this and thought that it would also work the other way round. He began by building a sort of transformer. In 1831, he invented a simpler machine to make an electric current from a magnet. This was the first dynamo. (*See* GENERATOR.) Joseph Henry also made a generator at the same time. All modern dynamos, generators, and transformers are based on the work of Faraday and Henry.

Faraday's work in chemistry was equally important. He discovered benzene in 1825. By combining his knowledge of chemistry and electricity he discovered the laws of electrolysis in 1834.

Two electrical units are named after Faraday. One is the faraday, used in measuring quantities of electricity. The other is the farad, a unit of capacitance. *See also* BENZENE; ELECTROLYSIS; FARAD. C.M./D.G.F.

Michael Faraday, the British physicist and chemist, is pictured in a contemporary photograph. Among Faraday's many important discoveries were the principles of the electric generator and the laws of electrolysis.

FARADAY CONSTANT (far′ ə dā kän′ stənt) The Faraday constant is the quantity of electricity that liberates one mole of a substance. (A mole of a substance is its atomic or molecular weight in grams.)

In electrolysis, a current of electricity is passed through a liquid, usually a solution. This causes some of the substances dissolved in the solution to leave the liquid. If the substance is a metal, it is deposited onto one of the electrodes. If it is a gas, the gas bubbles out of the liquid at one of the electrodes. The mass of the substance that is liberated depends on the quantity of electricity passed through the liquid.

The Faraday constant is the same for all substances. It is about 96,500 coulombs. For example, silver has an atomic weight of 108. Thus, 96,500 coulombs of electricity deposit 108 grams of silver. *See also* METER-KILO-GRAM-SECOND SYSTEM.   M.E./R.W.L.

FAT (fat) Fat is an important food for animals and plants. Fats can be found in animal tissues and in plants, especially in seeds. Fat is the main form in which animals, including human beings, store excess food for later use. Fats are made of the elements carbon, hydrogen, and oxygen. During digestion, fats are broken down into fatty acid and glycerol for use by the body. Because fats contain more carbon and hydrogen than do carbohydrates, they can supply more energy. Pure fat provides 8,907 calories per kilogram [4,040 calories per pound] compared to a carbohydrate which supplies 4,012 calories per kilogram [1,820 calories per pound]. (*See* CALORIE.) Though fats supply more than twice as many calories as carbohydrates, it is more difficult for the body to digest fats, and excess fats often end up being stored in the cells and tissues as body fat.

A fat is saturated or unsaturated, depending on whether the chemical bonds between the carbon atoms in the molecules contain all the hydrogen atoms they can hold (saturated)

PERCENTAGE FAT CONTENT OF FOODS			
Lard and suet	100	Salmon	13
Butter	84	Eggs	10
Brazil nuts	67	Oats	7
Walnuts	64	Halibut	5
Pork	about 55	Milk	4
Coconuts	51	Rice	2
Chocolate	48	Wheat	2
Peanuts	39	Potatoes	1
Cheese	27–37	Lemons	0.7
Lamb	about 23	Apples	0.5
Beef	13–22	Tomatoes	0.4
Poultry	16	Peaches	0.1

or could hold more (unsaturated). Most saturated fats are solid at room temperature. Unsaturated fats are liquids but can be made solid and saturated by adding hydrogen atoms (hydrogenation). Studies have shown that when saturated fats are eaten, the amount of cholesterol in the blood increases, but when unsaturated fats are eaten, the cholesterol is reduced. High levels of cholesterol are a contributing factor in development of the heart disease known as arteriosclerosis.

Body fat helps insulate against the cold. Fats are also used to make soap, candles, plastics, medicines, and many other products. Since fat dissolves in gasoline and benzene, these liquids are often used to remove oily or greasy dirt. *See also* DIET. A.J.C./J.J.F.

FATHOM (fath′ əm) A fathom is a unit of length used chiefly to measure water depth. One fathom equals 1.8 m [6 ft]. A fathom was originally measured as a distance between the fingertips of the hands when the arms are fully extended.   J.M.C./R.W.L.

FAULT (folt) A fault is a break or fracture in the earth's crust along which movement has occurred. Faults can move horizontally or vertically. This movement may sometimes cause an earthquake. In 1906, the San Andreas fault in California suddenly moved horizontally, causing a very destructive earthquake.

Faults shape the landscape by their

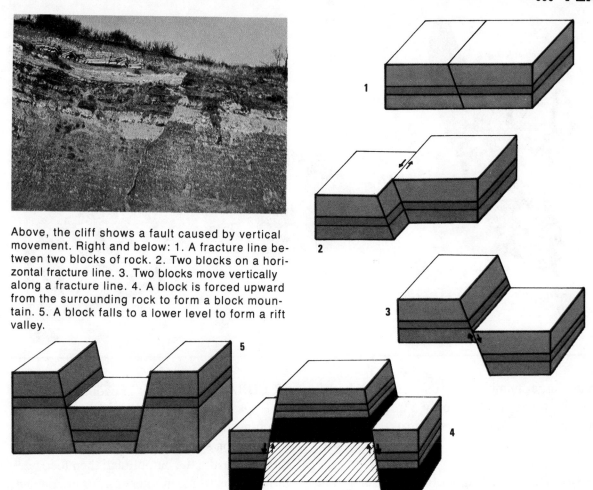

Above, the cliff shows a fault caused by vertical movement. Right and below: 1. A fracture line between two blocks of rock. 2. Two blocks on a horizontal fracture line. 3. Two blocks move vertically along a fracture line. 4. A block is forced upward from the surrounding rock to form a block mountain. 5. A block falls to a lower level to form a rift valley.

movements. When rocks on one side of a fault shift vertically, a fault scarp or ridge is formed on the uppermost surface. A block of land that rises between two faults is called a horst. A graben is a valley or depression that forms between two faults. A large graben is called a rift valley. *See also* CONTINENTAL DRIFT; EARTHQUAKE.   J.M.C./W.R.S.

FEATHER (feth′ ər) Feathers are specialized outgrowths from the skin found only in birds. Feathers are made of keratin and are probably evolved from the scales of prehistoric reptiles. (*See* EVOLUTION.) Feathers provide protection and warmth for the bird, as well as making it possible for it to fly. There are two kinds of feathers: down and contour. Down feathers are small and soft with fluffy "branches" growing out from a central point. Baby birds lose their down feathers as they grow older and develop contour feathers. Some water birds, such as ducks and geese, however, keep the down feathers as a layer beneath the contour feathers.

Contour feathers are arranged in symmetrical rows on the wings, body, and tail of the bird. A contour feather has a hollow quill embedded in the skin, and a flat vane. The vane has a strong, flexible central shaft called a rachis. Hundreds of barbs branch out from the rachis. From each of these barbs grow hundreds of barbules which interlock to hold the vane together as a continuous sheet. Often, a fluffy afterfeather arises from the top of the quill. In some contour feathers, there may not be interlocking barbules. A semi-plume

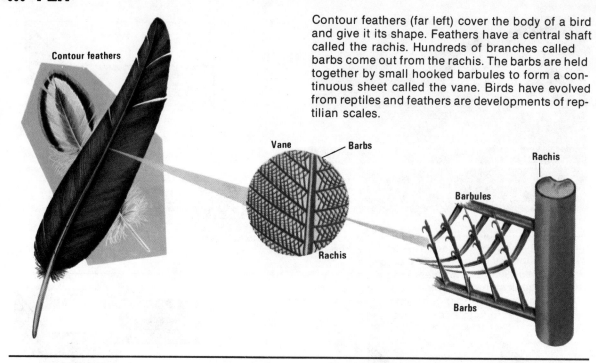

Contour feathers (far left) cover the body of a bird and give it its shape. Feathers have a central shaft called the rachis. Hundreds of branches called barbs come out from the rachis. The barbs are held together by small hooked barbules to form a continuous sheet called the vane. Birds have evolved from reptiles and feathers are developments of reptilian scales.

has large numbers of unconnected barbs, while filoplumes have only a tuft of barbs at the tip of the rachis. *See also* EGRET.

A.J.C./M.L.

FEATHER STAR (feth′ ər stär′) The feather star is any of several species of marine animals belonging to the phylum Echinodermata. Feather stars are related to starfish, but, like the sea lilies, they are crinoids. A feather star has a central disk, the bottom of which has a circle of tiny stalks called cirri. There are usually ten arms like tentacles each of which is covered by cilia and two rows of short, feathery branches. The mouth is on the upper surface of the disk and it receives a constant stream of tiny food particles filtered from the water by the cilia. (*See* PLANKTON.) Feather stars are able to move along the ocean floor by means of the cirri. Some are able to swim short distances by waving their arms.

Feather stars vary in size from 2.5 cm [1 in] to 90 cm [3 ft]. They live in both the Atlantic and Pacific Oceans, and range from the shallow, offshore waters to depths of about 1,370 m [4,500 ft]. A.J.C./C.S.H.

FEEDBACK (fēd′ bak′) Feedback is a principle used to control the work done by a machine or system. The work done by the machine or system is called output. Instruments measure the output, and then feed back information to a computer or a control device. The computer or control device compares the information with what the machine or system was originally directed to do. If the machine or system is not operating fast enough, for example, the computer or control device sends back a signal that makes it operate at a faster speed.

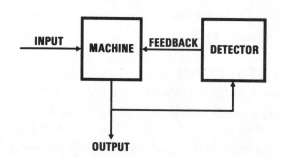

The feedback process: by detecting errors in output and sending a corrective feedback signal to a machine, a detector automatically controls the output. This process is followed by many information systems.

Feedback is important, for example, in a home heating system. The heart of the system is the furnace. It is controlled by an electric device called a thermostat. The thermostat is usually located on the first floor of the house. Sometimes individual rooms have their own thermostats. The thermostat is set at the desired temperature. If the room temperature where it is located becomes lower than the thermostat setting, the thermostat sends a signal that turns on the furnace. The furnace then warms the room and the rest of the house. After the room temperature has risen above the thermostat setting, the thermostat turns off the furnace.

Feedback in the field of automation depends on electrical instruments called sensors. Sensors measure temperatures, check size, weight, color, and chemical composition of products that are being manufactured. Each sensor sends back its information to a controlling computer. Engineers call this system a feedback control loop. The term loop refers to the flow of information in the system. The control loop goes from the computer, through the machine and its output, through the sensor, and finally back to the computer. Control loops can be closed loops or open loops. In the closed loop system, the computer automatically adjusts the operation of the machine, or system. In the open loop system, the computer activates a signal that may indicate trouble.

Feedback is also a term used in sound amplification. (*See* AMPLIFIER.) It occurs when the output sound signal from a microphone returns to the microphone, and causes a high-pitched squeal in the loudspeaker.

W.R.P./L.L.R.

FELDSPAR (fel′ spär′) Feldspars are the most common group of rock-forming minerals. Feldspar minerals make up more than half of all common igneous rocks, such as granite and basalt.

Feldspar usually occurs as glassy white, reddish, greenish, or bluish crystals. It is mined chiefly from pegmatite bodies. Pegmatite is a rock containing very large crystals of quartz and feldspar. In the United States, feldspar is mined in California, Connecticut, North Carolina, and South Carolina.

Albite is a common form of feldspar, found, among other places, in the Swiss and Italian Alps and in the Pikes Peak region of Colorado. It varies in color from white to grey.

Rocks containing feldspar break down when they are exposed to the atmosphere. This process is called weathering. They break down into other minerals, especially clay minerals. Much potassium is held in feldspars and in the soil produced by their weathering. Weathered feldspar is an important source of potassium which all plants need for growth. Clay materials derived from decomposed feldspar are used by pottery manufacturers to make porcelain and glass.

All feldspars consist of aluminum, silicon, and oxygen. The types of feldspar differ in the amounts and kinds of other elements that are present. Alkali feldspars contain potassium and sodium in various amounts. Green microcline, commonly known as amazonstone, is an alkali feldspar that is often cut and polished to make ornaments. Moonstone is a milky, translucent (light-admitting) alkali feldspar. People treasure moonstone as a gem. Plagioclase feldspars contain sodium and calcium in varying ratios.

Labradorite is a type of plagioclase that may show a range of vivid colors when light strikes it. Rocks containing such crystals are sometimes used to decorate buildings and are made into objects such as paperweights.

Albite, a common sodium-rich variety of plagioclase feldspar, varies in color from white to gray. It has been used in the manufacture of ceramics and also for making false teeth.   J.J.A./R.H.

FEMUR (fē′ mər) The femur is the longest, largest, and strongest bone in the human body. It is located in the upper leg and is sometimes called the thigh bone. It is joined to the pelvis by means of a ball-and-socket joint, and to the tibia by means of a hinge joint.   A.J.C./J.J.F.

FERMENTATION (fər′ mən tā′ shən) Fermentation is a change that takes place in vegetable or animal matter when chemicals called enzymes act upon it. The process of

Sauerkraut is made from cabbage which has been salted and fermented by bacteria in its own juice. It is a popular fermented food.

In this cheese-making machine, lactic acid bacteria ferment the cheese curd. This fermentation develops the flavor of the cheese.

fermentation changes the chemicals in the matter, and also changes the form, taste, and smell. Examples of fermentation include the ripening of cheese, the souring of milk, the change of apple juice to hard cider, and the change of alcohol in hard cider to vinegar. The enzymes that cause these changes are produced by the cells of plants and animals. Many come from bacteria and various other low forms of plants, like yeasts and molds. Familiar fermented foods include sauerkraut, chocolate, and buttermilk. Beer and wine are two of the best-known fermented liquids.

The action of yeast in bread dough is a type of fermentation. The enzyme from the yeast changes the starch in the flour to sugar. It then breaks down the sugar into carbon dioxide gas and alcohol. The gas forms bubbles which honeycomb the dough and puff it out until it rises.

Fermentation also aids the digestion of food. Gastric juices in the stomach contain the enzymes rennin and pepsin. Rennin curdles milk. Pepsin softens the albumen in food so that it dissolves in water and passes into the blood. When harmful bacteria enter the stomach, the acid in the gastric juices can usually destroy them. But if the acid is too weak, these bacteria ferment the food, and cause an attack of indigestion.

Growing plants are helped by the fermentation of dead plants and animals. Enzymes break down the chemical compounds . The elements return to the soil, and the plants use them over again. The breakdown of dead matter sometimes gives off bad odors, and the products may be poisonous. This type of fermentation is called putrefaction or anaerobic decomposition. W.R.P./J.M.

FERMI, ENRICO (1901–1954) Enrico Fermi (fär′ mē) was an Italian physicist. He studied nuclear physics and won the Nobel Prize for Physics in 1938. (*See* CHAIN REACTIONS.) He moved to America in 1939 and worked at Columbia University. In 1942,

after several years of work, he designed and operated the first nuclear power reactor. Today, nuclear power reactors are used to make electricity. Later on, during World War II, he helped to make the first atomic bomb. (*See* NUCLEAR WEAPONS.) A chemical element, called fermium, is named after him.

C.M./D.G.F.

FERMIUM (fər′ mē əm) Fermium (Fm) is a radioactive metallic element. It does not occur naturally and has to be made artificially. Only very small amounts of the metal have been made. This means that its melting and boiling points and its relative density are not yet known. Its atomic number is 100. Fermium was first discovered in the remains of a hydrogen bomb explosion in 1952. It is named after the Italian nuclear physicist, Enrico Fermi.

Fermium has ten isotopes. (*See* ISOTOPE.) The longest-lived isotope is fermium-257. This isotope has decayed by half in 80 days. No uses have yet been discovered for fermium. *See also* RADIOACTIVITY; TRANSURANIC ELEMENT. M.E./J.R.W.

Left, the hard fern

FERN (fərn) A fern is a vascular plant with roots, stems, and leaves, but no flowers or seeds. The more than 10,000 species are divided into 12 families, all of which belong to the large division of the plant kingdom called Pteridophyta. Fossils from the Carboniferous

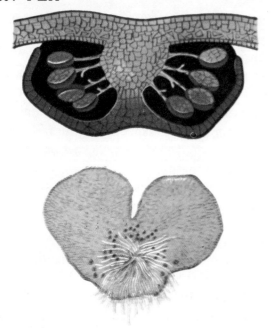

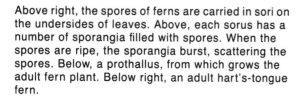

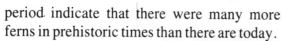

Above right, the spores of ferns are carried in sori on the undersides of leaves. Above, each sorus has a number of sporangia filled with spores. When the spores are ripe, the sporangia burst, scattering the spores. Below, a prothallus, from which grows the adult fern plant. Below right, an adult hart's-tongue fern.

period indicate that there were many more ferns in prehistoric times than there are today.

Ferns are found throughout the world, but seem to thrive in warm or tropical climates. They range in size from almost microscopic to the tree ferns which reach heights of more than 21 m [70 ft]. Some species grow on trees for support and rely on moisture in the air for survival. (*See* EPIPHYTE.) These are often called air ferns because they have no attachment to the ground. Most ferns, however, grow close to the ground, rarely reaching a height of more than 2 m [6.6 ft].

The stems and roots of ferns are usually underground. Some have specialized underground stems called rhizomes, which grow near the surface, producing many "subplants" along its length. The leaves, called fronds, are usually large and divided into leaflets. The fronds often have rows of

brownish sori which contain the sporangia, or spore cases. (*See* SPORANGIUM.) The sporangia contain the spores. When the spores mature, the sporangia open and the spores are spread by the wind. (*See* DISPERSION OF PLANTS.) Each spore develops into a tiny, heart-shaped plant called a prothallus. The prothallus is flat and disklike, with rootlike hairs on its bottom surface. Small reproductive structures then form on the prothallus. The male structure, the antheridium, produces a flagellated gamete called an antherozoid or sperm. (*See* FLAGELLUM.) The female structure, the archegonium, produces an egg. In moist conditions, the antherozoid "swims" to the archegonium where it fertilizes the egg. (*See* FERTILIZATION.) This zygote will develop into the large fern plant. This process—a spore-producing plant producing a gamete-producing plant which, in

turn, produces another spore-producing plant—is called alternation of generations.
A.J.C./M.H.S.

FERTILIZATION (fərt′ əl ə zā′ shən) Fertilization is the process in sexual reproduction in which a male gamete combines with a female gamete to produce a zygote. The zygote develops into a new organism. In animals, the male gamete is called a sperm (or spermatozoon) and is produced by the male sex organs, the testicles (or testes). The female gamete is called an egg (or ovum), and is produced in the female sex organs, the ovaries. Most land animals, including mammals, birds, and reptiles, practice internal fertilization, in which the male deposits sperm inside the female's body, where it joins with the egg. Most aquatic animals, however, practice external fertilization. The female lays eggs in the water and the male spreads sperm over them. The sperm will swim around until they fertilize an egg. Since many sperm and eggs never meet, external fertilizers usually produce great numbers of gametes to improve chances of fertilization. Some animals are hermaphrodites, and produce both male and female gametes. Some hermaphrodites are able to fertilize their own eggs.

In flowering plants, angiosperms, the male gamete is called pollen and is produced by the anther, part of the stamen. The female gamete, the egg, is produced in the ovary of the pistil. During fertilization, pollen is transported to the pistil. (*See* DISPERSION OF PLANTS; POLLINATION.) The pollen grows a tube through the style of the pistil to the ovary where it fertilizes the egg. In gymnosperms, non-flowering seed plants, pollen from male cones fertilizes eggs in female cones. These female cones than protect the zygote as it develops into a seed. In lower plants, there is often alternation of generations in which a spore-producing generation alternates with a gamete-producing generation. The gamete-producing generation usually includes the antheridium which produces male gametes, and the archegonium which produces female gametes. (*See* FERN.) In most lower plants, and some higher plants, both male and female structures are on the same plant. In some cases, one flower may have both male and female structures. In such a case, the flower rarely fertilizes itself because the reproductive structures mature at different times, or because the structure of the flower itself makes transfer of pollen from anther to pistil difficult. *See also* REPRODUCTION; SEX.
A.J.C./E.R.L.

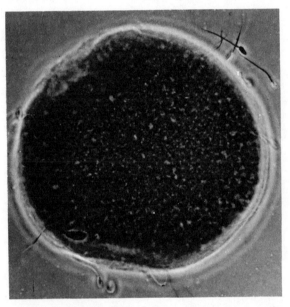

This magnified picture of an ovum shows a spermatazoon penetrating it to fertilize it.

FERTILIZER (fərt′ əl ī′ zər) A fertilizer is a substance added to the soil to improve the growth of plants. About 95% of the fertilizer produced in the world is used in farming. In order for plants to grow, photosynthesis must take place. In order for photosynthesis to occur, plants must be supplied with certain nutrients. Macronutrients are those nutrients which plants use in fairly large quantities. These include carbon, hydrogen, oxygen, potassium, phosphorous, nitrogen, calcium, sulfur, and magnesium. Plants need only small amounts of micronutrients such as manganese, molybdenum, zinc, iron, copper, and boron. Air and water are primary sources for carbon, hydrogen, and oxygen, but the other nutrients must come from the soil.

If soil is deficient in any of the macronutrients or micronutrients, fertilizers containing these elements must be added. Fertilizers are one of two types: synthetic or organic

Synthetic fertilizers are made from minerals and contain controlled amounts of specific nutrients, usually phosphorous, nitrogen, and potassium. Phosphorous fertilizers are made from the mineral apatite. If apatite is mixed with phosphoric or sulfuric acid, a liquid fertilizer called superphosphate results. Most synthetic nitrogen comes from ammonia and ammonia-containing compounds. Most of the potassium is manufactured from potassium chloride. Lime (calcium hydroxide) is often added to the soil to neutralize acidity. (*See* NEUTRALIZATION.)

Organic fertilizers are usually made from manure, plant matter, animal matter, or sewage. (*See* SEWAGE TREATMENT.) They provide nitrogen and some other nutrients, but in varying amounts. Since organic fertilizers have a smaller percentage of the needed nutrients, larger amounts must be used. Animal manure is often mixed with straw and allowed to rot before it is used. Guano (bird droppings) is also used as a fertilizer in many areas. Plant matter is sometimes made into a compost pile by adding layers of soil and lime. Bacteria begin to decay the plant matter in the compost pile, releasing needed nutrients. Green manure is actually plants that are grown and then plowed into the ground to restore nutrients. Crops of legumes such as alfalfa, clover, and beans are often grown for this purpose in a process of crop rotation. Animal matter such as bone meal and dried blood is sometimes used as an organic fertilizer. Because it is too expensive to use on a large scale, animal matter is usually used by home gardeners. *See also* FOOD CHAIN; NITROGEN CYCLE. A.J.C./F.W.S.

FEVER (fē′ vər) Fever is a condition in which the body temperature rises above the normal 37°C [98.6°F]. It is a common symptom of disease. The first signs of a fever are chills, loss of appetite, and a general feeling of weakness. This is accompanied by a rise in temperature, rapid pulse, headache, and restlessness. The patient may be uncomfortable during this stage, sometimes called the height of the fever. Soon the body temperature falls back to normal, and the patient often falls asleep. A fever may affect a patient continuously for several days, or it may disappear for a few days, only to return again.

Fevers are often the symptom of a serious infection. Some diseases, like scarlet fever, are so named because the high fever is the most apparent symptom. *See also* DISEASE. J.M.C./J.J.F.

FIBER

A fiber (fī′ bər) is a threadlike strand of a substance. For example, in examining cotton thread on a spool, it can be shown that the thread is made up of hundreds of very short fibers twisted together. Most fabrics are made by gathering a collection of short, fine fibers and twisting them into a firm yarn.

Some fibers are found in nature. Others are artificial. The chemical make-up and arrangement of molecules in a fiber determine its properties. Properties of a fiber include absorbency, strength, and stretchability.

There are two basic forms of fibers. They are based on length. Staples measure from about 1.3 to 20 cm [0.5 to 8 in] in length. Some staples, however, are more than 100 cm [40 in] long. Most of the fibers occurring in nature are staples. The other major form of fibers, continuous filaments, range from more

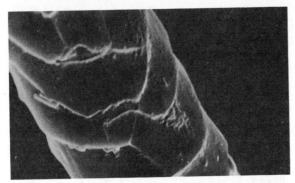

Above, a strand of sheep's wool magnified 2,600 times.

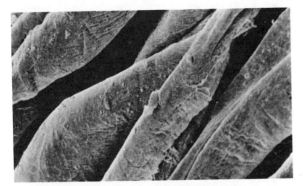

Above, cotton fibers magnified 2,600 times.

The photograph below shows the seed boll, or pod, of a cotton plant.

than 270 m [300 yd] in length for silk fibers to indefinite lengths for artificial fibers.

Natural fibers Natural fibers come from plants, animals, and minerals. The most widely used of all natural fibers is cotton. Cotton comes from the seed boll, or pod, of the cotton plant. Staples from cotton are spun into yarns for clothing and many other fabrics. Cotton cloth is absorbent and soft. Linen is made from fibers obtained from the stalks of flax plants. Fibers obtained from flax are called bast fibers. Hemp and jute are also bast fibers. Hemp, jute, and sisal are coarse fibers used in cords, ropes, and rough fabrics.

Fibers obtained from animals include hair and fur. Wool, obtained from sheep, is widely used in clothing. Wool resists creasing and crushing. Its fibers uncurl when stretched, but return to their original state when released. Also each fiber is covered with rough scales. Rough surfaces on wool fibers give bulk and warmth to wool clothing and blankets. Silk is

also an important animal fiber. It is the strongest natural fiber. Silk is unique among natural fibers because it is produced in a long, continuous thread called a filament. Manufacturers unwind silk filaments from silkworm cocoons. Silk yarn is used for clothing and household fabrics. Other animals supply useful fibers. Cashmere, obtained from certain goats, is used in making knitwear. Mohair, a fabric made from the hair of the Angora goat, is used in lightweight suits. Camel hair, also used in the manufacture of suits, is the hair of certain animals, such as the alpaca and llama of South America.

Above, the South American llama has thick woolly hair which is widely used to make blankets and fabrics for clothes.

Above, a sheep shearer is using mechanical clippers to remove wool from a sheep. Sheep's wool is the commonest fiber taken from animals.

Various minerals that occur in fibrous form are called asbestos. Being fire-resistant, such fibers are used in insulation and shingles.

Manufactured fibers Many of the manufactured fibers are plastics. In studying plastics, chemists have learned how to combine chemicals to make fibers which have certain properties. Such chemicals are melted or mixed in various liquids. Machines force streams of the chemicals through tiny holes. (*See* EXTRUSION.)

There are two main types of manufactured fibers. In the first group are fibers processed by people, but derived from natural materials, such as plant cellulose. Cellulosics is the name for fibers that come from cellulose. The most familiar of this group is rayon. Rayon has many properties that resemble cotton. Acetate is produced by treating cellulose with acetic acid. Acetate is a silky fiber. Both rayon and acetate are used in clothing. Rayon has also been used in the manufacture of tires.

The second group of manufactured fibers are those made entirely from materials produced by people. These are called synthetic fibers. Synthetic fibers are sometimes called noncellulosics. Nylon fibers were the first synthetic fibers. Lightweight and very strong, nylon is widely used in the manufacture of carpets, ropes, tires, and clothing. Polyester fibers are durable and regain their shape after being stretched or wrinkled. Dacron and Kodel are types of polyester. Acrylic fibers, such as Acrilan and Orlon, are soft and durable. Many imitation furs and wools are made from acrylic fibers. Olefin fibers are strong and stain resistant. These properties make olefin fibers such as Herculon useful in carpets and upholstery.

Fiberglass is a synthetic fiber made from glass. When woven, it is quite strong and

Facing right, silkworms feed on the leaves of a mulberry tree. At the bottom of the picture is a silkworm cocoon. A silkworm can make more than 3,000 feet of silk.

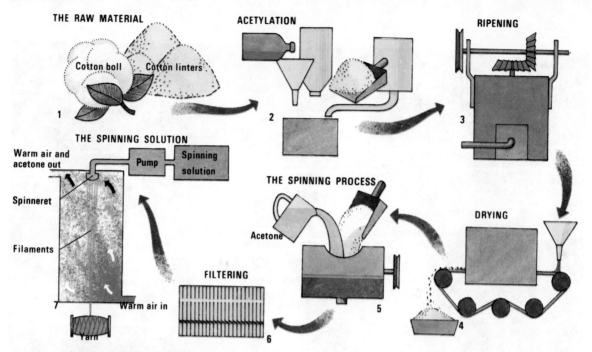

THE RAW MATERIAL — Cotton boll — Cotton linters — 1

ACETYLATION — 2

RIPENING — 3

THE SPINNING SOLUTION — Warm air and acetone out — Pump — Spinning solution — Spinneret — Filaments — Warm air in — Yarn — 7

THE SPINNING PROCESS — Acetone — 5

DRYING — 4

FILTERING — 6

The manufacture of acetate rayon. 1. Cotton linters (unspinnable fibers) contain cellulose. 2. The linters are dissolved in acetic acid and other chemicals to form cellulose acetate. 3. The acetate solution is ripened and made into flakes by adding water.

4. The flakes are dried by rollers. 5. The flakes are dissolved in acetone to form a spinning solution and (6) the solution is filtered. The spinning solution is forced through the holes of a spinneret to make filaments for yarn.

Sheets of wood pulp, which is almost pure cellulose, are stacked in an Australian fiber factory.

resists stretching. (*See* FIBERGLASS.) Yarns called Lastex are made from manufactured rubber fibers wrapped in cotton, nylon, or other fibers.

Although synthetic fibers have replaced natural fibers in many instances, it is unlikely that natural fibers will go out of use. Certain properties in natural fibers, such as the warmth and texture of superior wool, have not yet been fully matched by synthetic fibers.

J.J.A./M.H.S.

FIBERGLASS (fī′ bər glas′) Fiberglass is an artificial material composed of tiny threads of glass. It is strong, durable, and fireproof. Fiberglass is used for such things as curtains, because it is waterproof and needs no ironing.

The first step in making fiberglass is to melt glass marbles in an electric furnace. The melted glass goes out small holes in the bottom of the furnace, where it is caught by a spinning drum. The high speed of the drum forces the melted glass into fine fibers. These fibers are then processed according to their intended use.

Fiberglass is an excellent insulator. (*See*

INSULATION.) Many people insulate their homes with fiberglass to conserve energy. *See also* EXTRUSION.   J.M.C./A.D.

Molded fiberglass can be used to make an automobile body (below).

Strips of glass wool made from fiberglass are laid on the floor of an attic to give better heat insulation for a house. Glass wool has been wrapped around the cold water tank to prevent the water from freezing in winter.

FIBER OPTICS (fī′ bər äp′ tiks) Fiber optics is a relatively new branch of physics. It deals with the transmission of light through hair-thin glass tubes called optical fibers. Optical fibers have many uses in science and industry. But their most important application is in the field of communications.

It was communications engineers and physicists who first thought of transmitting light in this way. They saw the need for inventing a special material for carrying light from place to place. To do this, they sought the help of a glass manufacturer. The combined skills of engineers from Bell Laboratories and the Corning Glass Works accomplished the task. By 1970, after much hard work, these scientists had made a strong, suitable optical fiber. This fiber could carry a light signal 2.5 km (1.6 mi) before an amplifier was needed to strengthen the signal. Telecommunications via optical fibers had become a reality.

Optical fibers are flexible glass tubes cov-

ered with a sleeve of special insulating material. The inside walls serve as mirrors. They reflect rays of light back and forth across the hollow core. This enables the light to travel along a curved path, or even around corners.

The light source used with optical fibers may be a tiny laser or a light-emitting diode (LED). In a telephone system, the light source is equivalent to the transmitter in radio communication. But the sound is changed to light waves instead of radio waves. At the receiving end, the light signals are changed back to sound. Complex electronic equipment is involved.

Optical fibers have an advantage over the copper wire conductor. Since they do not use electric current, there is no electro-magnetic interference. They are lightweight and take up little space. They are also useful in lighting hard-to-reach spaces. H.S.B./G.D.B.

These thin optical fibers transmit light. The thick part at the bottom is a special insulating material.

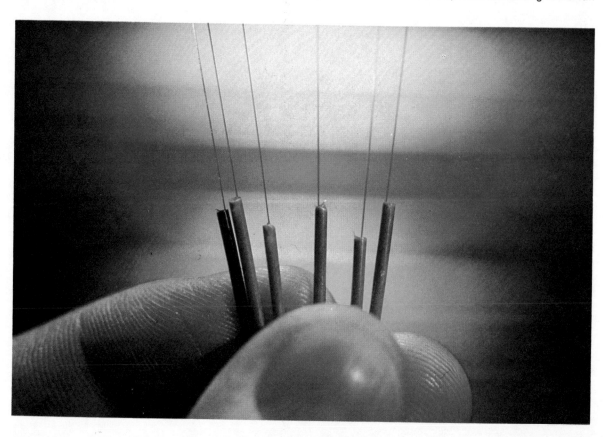

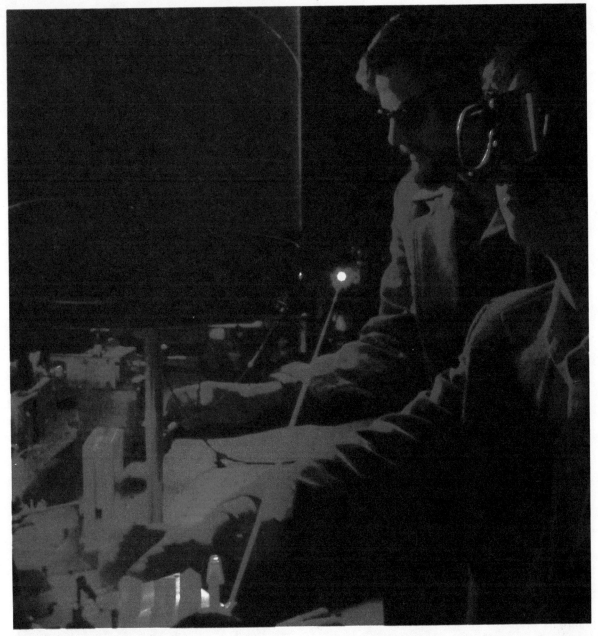

These scientists at Bell Laboratories are operating a fiber-optic laser used in the development of a new telephone communications system.

FIBULA (fib′ yə lə) The fibula is a long, fairly thin bone that is the outer of the two bones in the lower leg. It is joined to the other, larger bone, the tibia, by ligaments at both ends. In addition, the fibula and tibia are joined by a membrane that extends the length of the bones. The lower end of the fibula forms the "bump" on the outer part of the ankle.   A.J.C./J.J.F.

FIELD (fēld) In physics, the word "field" is used to describe a region in which a force can have an effect on a body without any contact being made with that body. For example, small pieces of iron placed a short distance from a magnet are attracted toward the magnet. This action is said to be due to the presence of a magnetic or force field.

Such a field can be investigated by sprinkling iron filings on a piece of card held over a magnet. The filings form patterns. These patterns show the lines of magnetic force joining the north and south poles of the magnet. (*See* MAGNETISM.) A magnetic field is also set up when an electric current flows through a wire. (*See* ELECTROMAGNETISM.)

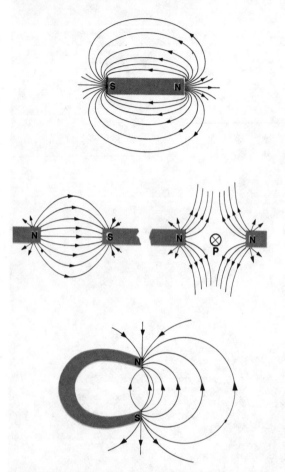

Lines of force in a magnetic field. Notice that unlike poles repel each other, and like poles attract each other, as shown by the lines of force.

Near an electric charge, a charged particle experiences a force. The region in which this occurs is called an electric field. The force may be one of attraction or repulsion. This depends on whether the charges are like or unlike. Unlike charges—that is, one positive and one negative change—are attracted. Like charges repel each other.

An electric field, like a magnetic field, can be represented by lines of force. Electrostatic fields can be examined by placing a light-weight, charged ball in the field and watching how it moves. (*See* ELECTROSTATICS.)

A gravitational field is the region in which a gravitational force of attraction can be detected between bodies. This force depends on the mass of the objects and their distance apart. The moon is in the earth's gravitational field. The moon is kept in its orbit by the gravitational force of attraction between itself and the earth. (*See* GRAVITY.)　　J.J.A./A.I.

FIG (fig) The fig is any of 1,800 species of tropical and subtropical plants belonging to the genus *Ficus* of the mulberry family. The most common fig, *Ficus carica*, is a deciduous tree that ranges in height from 1 to 12 m [3.3 to 40 ft]. It has large, rough leaves and produces an edible, pear-shaped fruit in the axils. This fruit is actually a hollow receptacle which contains hundreds of tiny flowers. These flowers are fertilized by insects such as the gall wasps which bore into the receptacle to lay eggs. (*See* POLLINATION.)

Figs were some of the earliest cultivated fruits. They remain an important food in many Mediterranean countries, and can be eaten fresh, dried, or preserved. Figs have a mild laxative effect and are a good source of bulk in the diet. In the United States, most figs are grown in California and Texas. *See also* BANYAN.　　A.J.C./F.W.S.

Figs grow well in Mediterranean climates. They are often eaten dried.